Dear Reader:

When deadly pandemics (such as the Spanish Flu of 1918 and, more recently, COVID-19) strike the world, many people feel helpless against them. Masks, vaccinations, social distancing, quarantining, and more have all been tried with varying degrees of success. Yet infectious diseases march on – often with tragic results. This most recent "cauldron of contagion" has led many to ask, "what can I do to improve my own chances when a virus threatens the world?"

While we all recognize that:

- **Everyone's personal health scenario is different (e.g. some individuals, due to certain risk factors, are already more susceptible to disease), and**
- **There are no guarantees in this life (e.g. someone may successfully stave off infectious disease, only to be hit by a train.)**

There is good news, and even reason for hope! While we can't control everything that might happen to us in this life, even a person who is already ill can implement a series of changes that can potentially improve immune system function. Every day of your life, certain choices you make have a deep impact on your body's ability to fight off disease. For those who are already stricken, even a positive outlook has been shown to be beneficial.

Many of the best immune-building strategies are forgotten – but tried-and-true – remedies from decades gone by. Others are cutting edge, evidence-based treatments that are receiving increasingly strong backing from scientific research.

"But I'm vaccinated," some say. "That's all I need." Or, "I've got natural immunity, since I already fought my way through a bout with the latest strain of infection." The reality is that, in the face of mutating viruses, pathogens, and newly emerging infectious diseases, more than one strategy is needed to ward off impending health threats. Each of us needs all the weaponry we can muster in our immune-boosting arsenal.

Regardless of vaccination status, personal belief systems, or individual health challenges, every person on this planet stands to benefit by implementing a series of simple but powerful steps that can help build a stronger immune system.

In our book Pandemic Busters we outlined 22 simple and easy immune boosting strategies that anyone can do in their home.

That book was organized in a way meant to:

- **Show by example that some simple remedies have been successful in combating past pandemics (including the Spanish Flu),**
- **Provide information speedily and in an order that might be of the most benefit to the greatest number of readers, and,**
- **End with some incredibly important information on how faith, hope, an optimistic outlook on life, and yes – even laughter – can dramatically improve immune system function.**

In contrast, the Pandemic Busters Workbook is organized in a manner meant for a class setting with Pandemic Busters as the textbook. The worksheets, charts, and illustrations are designed to help readers with the practical side of applying things learned. It is our sincere hope that this workbook will help you to implement the simple but powerful immune-boosting strategies with the potential to have the most profound and positive impact on your personal health.

To your healthiest life,

Eddie Ramirez, M.D.
Cari Haus

Copyright © 2022 by:

HealthWhys Lifestyle Medicine
2363 Mountain Road
Hamburg, Pennsylvania 19526

First Printing

For permission or bulk copy requests, contact the publisher, addressed **"Attention: Permissions Coordinator,"** at this address: info@healthwhys.com or **call (610) 685-9900**, or visit our website at http://www.healthwhys.com.

Cover and Interior Design: Olena Lykova

ISBN: 978-1-955866-03-3

Chapter Assignments:
1: Study History – Or You May Be Deleted
2: Go to Bed – Find the Healing Power of Sleep

What You'll Learn:
At the end of this session, you will have a better understanding of:

Chapter 1:
- Virus-stopping remedies that were more successful than others in the face of the deadliest pandemic in modern times (the Spanish Flu of 1918)
- Why the mortality rates at some hospitals were much lower than others during that modern pandemic
- An introduction to the remedies that worked "back then" and why they could still help today

Chapter 2:
- The critical relationship between sleep and immune system function
- The impact of disrupted work routines during the recent pandemic and circadian rhythms (and why that matters to you)
- The strong connection between sleep habits and insomnia, depression, and other health challenges
- Easy, simple-to-follow tips for improving your sleep habits and, with them, the effectiveness of your immune system response to various disease threats, including influenza, coronaviruses and their variants.

Bonus Sections:
- Why the Spanish Flu Mattered
- Joined at the "Sleep" (The Sleep-Immune System Connection)

Worksheets:
- Multiple Choice (or Not!)
- True – or Alternative Fact?
- Mortality Matching
- Self-Rating Scale
- Steps You Can Take
- Action Plan
- Other Points to Remember

Why the Spanish Flu Mattered

Just before breakfast on March 4 of 1918, Private Albert Gitchell reported to the United States Army Hospital in Fort Riley, Kansas with cold-like symptoms. By noon of that day, more than a hundred of Private Gitchell's fellow soldiers had experienced a similar malady. The fever, headaches, and sore throats described by these military men as they streamed into the army hospital are now believed to be some of the first cases of the highly-lethal "Spanish Flu" which ravaged much of the world that year.[1]

The deadliest pandemic in recent history, the Spanish Flu infected at least a third of the world's population during its rampage.[2] Estimates of the total death toll, which originally stood at around 20 million people, are now considered to be ridiculously low by most standards. As new historical records have come to light, the fatality count has ballooned to between 50 and 100 million people.[3] To put things in perspective, the Spanish Flu killed more soldiers during World War I than combat.[4]

In contrast to the seasonal flu (which is more likely to take the elderly or infirm), the Spanish Flu was most lethal to young people in their prime. Ninety-nine percent of Spanish Flu victims were 65 years old or younger; many were only in their twenties and thirties.[5] Some localities (such as the state of Alaska, where 50% of adult residents died), were hit particularly hard.[6]

At the peak of the outbreak, more than 25% of patients in one Philadelphia hospital died each night, many without seeing a nurse or doctor.[7] Morgues (some of which were handling 10 times their normal capacity) were overflowing. Gravediggers, who often themselves came down with the flu, couldn't keep up with the requests for burials. Coffins and morticians were also in short supply.[8]

The demands of wartime had resulted in many doctors being called into military service. The shortage of nurses was even more severe. As they were stretched to the limit, the available medical staff began to fall ill themselves. As a result, patient care rapidly deteriorated.[9] To replenish the supply of doctors, some states took creative — even desperate — measures. The timing of medical school graduations and exams was moved up, and some dentists were authorized to work as physicians.[10]

Attempts at therapy for flu victims brought into the hospitals were described as "exercises in futility." In the standard hospital setting, there were few effective treatments for those infected. In an era lacking effective vaccines or drugs, the view of modern medicine was and still is that, in the case of the Spanish Flu, there was little physicians could do for their patients.[11]

While much of the record of the Spanish Flu details its horrors and high mortality rates, together with the inability of medicine to save the sick, there were hospitals where the deadly virus was staved off with truly amazing success. Many of the hospitals with the most effective treatment programs were known as sanitariums. With a protocol featuring lifestyle changes and natural remedies, these sanitariums experienced extremely low mortality rates compared to the rest of the world.[12] Most of these sanitariums were run by Seventh-day Adventists (such as the famous Battle Creek Sanitarium, run by Dr. John Harvey Kellogg). With their unique perspective on health, these are the same people that today form the core of America's Blue Zone™ region in Loma Linda, California. (Being in a Blue Zone™ means that, due to healthy lifestyle choices, they live on average a decade longer than other Americans).[13]

Joined at the Sleep

It seemed like a wonderful idea. Peter Tripp, a top New York DJ in the 1950's, would raise money for the March of Dimes (a children's foundation) by setting a new world record. His plan? To broadcast from inside a glass booth in Times Square for 201 straight hours. During the Wake-a-thon, Tripp would be monitored by medical personnel. The public would also be free to stop by.

At the start of Tripp's time in the giant "fishbowl" he was in jovial spirits. The good mood didn't last for long, however. By the third day, he was not only hallucinating, but cursing at those nearby. Becoming convinced that there were spiders in his shoes, Tripp took them off to check. Over the course of the sleeplessness marathon (which he did complete) Tripp progressed from hallucinations and paranoia to full-blown psychosis.

When it was all over, Tripp caught 13 hours of much-needed shut-eye, then declared himself no worse for the wear. His family and friends weren't so sure, however. They said Tripp was a changed man—and they appeared to be right. After the stunt, Tripp began to think he was an imposter of himself—an opinion he held for quite some time. Not long after, he lost both his job and his marriage. After several failed attempts to re-establish himself as a radio personality, Tripp eventually finished his career as a traveling salesman. He did remarry, but sadly, was also divorced three additional times.[14]

The story of Peter Tripp is just one of many that emphasize the impact of sleep—or the lack thereof—on the human body. All too often, well-meaning people who miss sleep end up in difficult places. It's a well-known fact that a number of famous accidents (such as Chernobyl and the Exxon Valdez) were related to sleep deprivation.[15]

What isn't as well known is the highly important role sleep plays in boosting the immune system. More light has been shed on this topic in recent years. As researchers have delved ever more deeply into the science of sleep, the strong connection between getting enough zzz's and immune system function has become increasingly clear.[16]

The Immune System Connection

As it turns out, your immune system and sleeping patterns have a circular "cause and effect" relationship. When you are trying to fight off a "bug," your immune response (such as runny nose, headache, or a fever) may make it difficult for you to sleep. On the other side of the coin, sleep difficulties such as insomnia or sleep apnea lower the immune system, making it more likely that you will catch the bug in the first place.[17] Should you fall ill, lack of sleep can also lengthen your recovery time.[18]

In order to have the best immune system response—and ward off threats such as COVID-19—the body must be healthy enough to not only detect threats, but to fight against them. As is discussed in Pandemic Busters, sleep is one of the most important tools to help the body maintain that much-needed level of health.

While You Are Sleeping...

Much like a time-deprived parent, your body switches into high gear whenever it gets the chance. There's a lot of cleaning, repairing, picking up, and yes—even resting—to be done while you sleep. Many of those bodily "chores" contribute to not only a healthier you, but a stronger immune system. The amount—and quality—of your sleep will greatly impact your ability not only to fight off the latest virus, but to ward off its evil sisters who may bang on your door as well.

Researchers have found that certain bodily defenses "rev up" while we sleep.[19] For instance, the body makes more cytokines at night.[20] Whether you're sick, injured, or simply trying to fight off an infection, this cytokine-related inflammatory response fortifies the body and helps it to heal.[21]

Scientists have also found that sleeping strengthens the "memory" of the immune system, helping it to better recognize—and ward off—pathogens.[22]

The fact that your muscle and breathing activity slow down while you sleep gives the body's defenses more energy to perform the needed "maintenance."[23] Adequate nightly zzz's help reduce the impact of allergic reactions, and they can even help your body to have a more efficient response to vaccines.[24, 25] Sleep also allows your body to produce more melatonin, which in turn not only aids more sleep, but works to reduce inflammatory stress.[26]

Consequences of Sleep Deprivation

Missing out on much-needed shut-eye results in a wide range of health-damaging consequences for your body. While good sleep improves the immune system response, lack of sleep has the exact opposite effect, making you more vulnerable to getting sick.

In addition to short-term illnesses, researchers have connected poor sleeping habits with chronic illnesses such as diabetes and heart disease.[27] These diseases have been linked, in turn, to a higher risk of contracting a severe case of COVID-19.

Individuals who get less than 6-7 hours of sleep per night have also been shown to run a higher risk of infection.[28]

The Good News About Sleep

If you find yourself lacking in this important immune-boosting department of your life, "rest assured" that by taking some simple but positive steps, you can significantly improve the quality of your sleep—and with it, your body's defenses against virus and pathogen threats.

"A good laugh and a long sleep are the best cures in the doctor's book."

Multiple Choice (or Not!)

After reviewing the chapter assignments, circle the correct answer(s) for each of the questions below. (Note – some questions have more than one right answer.)

1. Deadly pandemics have:
a. Never happened before COVID-19
b. Taken many lives throughout the history of this world
c. Sometimes tipped the balance of political power
d. Only impacted one town at a time

2. The Spanish Flu of 1918:
a. Killed more soldiers than the war did during World War I
b. Originated in Spain
c. Is known as the most lethal pandemic in modern history
d. Was most lethal to elderly people

3. During World War I, wounded soldiers treated in open air hospitals had:
a. Regular attacks of diarrhea
b. Higher mortality rates than those treated indoors
c. Lower mortality rates than those treated indoors
d. A high risk of hypothermia

4. Sanitariums mimicked the best features of open air hospitals through the use of:
a. High ceilings
b. Double shifts for all doctors and nurses
c. Fresh air and good ventilation
d. Large windows that let in sunlight

5. Spanish Flu sufferers who were moved outside into the sunshine on nice days:
a. Died very quickly
b. Added sunburn to their list of maladies
c. Often showed remarkable improvement in as little as one day
d. Hated every minute of it

6. The sanitariums (and seminary) that treated Spanish Flu victims so successful fed their patients:
e. Ice cream at every meal
f. The Weight Watchers™ plan
g. A simple plant-based diet
h. Bacon and eggs for strength

7. When you are asleep, your body:
a. Increases interferon production
b. Switches into high gear and "cleans house"
c. Strengthens its immune system
d. All of the above.

8. A disruption in the body's circadian rhythm:
a. Impacts the regulation of every cell in the body
b. Disrupts digestion, immune response, and sleep
c. Both of the above
d. None of the above

9. Results of lost sleep include:
a. Lower performance and slower reaction time
b. Better performance and faster reaction time
c. Decreased immune system function
d. Higher risk of diabetes, heart disease, and obesity

10. People who get less than 7 hours of sleep per night:
a. Run a greater risk of infection
b. Are more likely to die prematurely
c. Run a greater risk of depression
d. All the above

11. Better sleep habits have been linked to:
a. Enhanced immune system function
b. Improved memory and longer attention span
c. Success in the political arena
d. Less stress and a happier life

12 When you sleep, the two main phases of sleep (REM and non-REM) work together to:
a. Speed the digestive process
b. Spark creativity by finding unrecognized links between facts
c. Increase personal coping skills
d. Create new bone marrow

True – or Alternative Fact?

Circle the correct True or False answer for each of the statements below:

1.	Open air military hospitals were more successful at treating the Spanish Flu than their indoor counterparts.	True	False
2.	Good hydration (e.g. drinking lots of water) was an important part of the treatment regimen at the sanitariums that treated the Spanish Flu so successfully.	True	False
3.	The body's muscles and breathing activities slow down while you sleep, giving the body time to perform needed maintenance.	True	False
4.	The fact that the "master clock" of the body (circadian rhythm) goes "out of whack" has no real impact on health or immune system function.	True	False
5.	Melatonin, which is created when the body sleeps, helps to boost the immune system by reducing inflammation in the body.	True	False
6.	Stay-at-home orders and working from home have nothing to do with circadian rhythm.	True	False
7.	The better you sleep, the stronger your immune system.	True	False
8.	The stronger your immune system, the better you sleep.	True	False
9.	Insomnia and depression are not related at all.	True	False
10.	Only 10% of the world's population have a sleep disorder.	True	False

Mortality Matching

If you lived in 1918 and came down with the Spanish Flu, your odds of a speedy demise varied greatly depending on where you were taken. Draw lines to match the appropriate mortality rate to each of the medical treatment options below:

GENERAL HOSPITAL	**1.3%**
SANITARIUM	**6-7%**
OPEN AIR MILITARY HOSPITAL	**13-40%**

Self-Rating Scale

INSTRUCTIONS: Circle the answer that fits you best.

	😊	😐	☹️	😢
When I feel like I might be coming down with a "bug," I normally:	Act quickly	Take cautious action	Keep an eye on things	Ignore it
The amount of restful sleep I usually get is:	7+ hours nightly	6 hours nightly	5 hours nightly	Less than 4 hours
When trying to fight a virus, I normally:	Tuck myself into bed!	Try to get extra rest	Slow down a little	Blast straight ahead!
I've used some type of heat or hydrotherapy to kills germs in the past:	Always	Frequently	Sometimes	Never
I go outside and breathe clean, fresh air:	All the time	Quite a bit	Once in a while	Hardly ever
The indoor areas where I spend the most time are abundant in clean, fresh air:	Always	Most of the time	Sometimes	Not at all
I get out and enjoy the sunshine:	Frequently	Not as much as I should	Sometimes	Not!
I drink plenty of pure, fresh water:	Always	Most of the time	Sometimes	That's my Achilles heel!
My usual diet is:	Simple and easy to digest	Simple most of the time	Swings between good and bad	Rich and hard digest

Review your answers in the previous section. Are there any simple and/or immediate steps you can take to improve in any of these areas? If so, list them below:

Steps I Can Take:

1 _____

_____

_____

2 _____

_____

_____

3 _____

_____

_____

4 _____

_____

_____

5 _____

_____

_____

_____

Action Plan

Review the "Action Plan" from chapters 1 and 2 as summarized below.
Put a check mark by the ones you are ready to work on:

○ Find ways you can get more fresh air at home and at work and put them into action. Do the same for sunlight.

○ Consider your normal strategy when trying to fight off a "bug." If rest and non-drug therapies haven't been high on your list in the past, make a plan in advance to try some new things.

○ Get whatever you need – and have it on hand, for any therapies you plan to try. If sleep is not a priority in your life, make and implement a plan to change that.

○ Compare your own sleep habits to the good and bad habits discussed in Chapter 2. Design and implement a plan to improve your sleep.

○ Consider and write down what health benefits you may gain by getting more and better sleep. Use this as your motivation!

Other Points to Remember

Are there other points you would like to remember from the chapters covered in this session? If so, write them here:

_____

_____

_____

_____

_____

_____

_____

_____

_____

Reading Assignments:
Chapter 3: Run a Fever: Sometimes Its Just What You Need
Chapter 4: Soak – Steam – Detox: The Incredible Healing Power of Water

What You'll Learn:
At the end of this session, you will have a better understanding of:

Chapter 3:
- The 7 benefits of letting a fever run its course
- How fevers were used as "medicine" throughout history
- What your body is really trying to accomplish by "ramping up" the heat
- Reasons why you might want to artificially raise your body temp, plus 5 ways to do it
- 4 problems created by knocking down a fever with meds
- Natural ways to lower a fever
- Fever therapy (hyperthermia) as an up-and-coming cancer treatment

Chapter 4:
- Why the Finns (and other Scandinavians) love saunas so much
- The many healing benefits of water therapy (hydrotherapy), inside and out
- Why ice baths and "polar plunges" have been so popular during pandemic times
- 5 inexpensive and easy ways to do hydrotherapy at home
- Why good hydration is so key to overall health

Bonus Sections:
- When an Outsider Gave Medical Orders
- New Study Highlights Water Treatment as a Potential Ally in the Fight Against COVID-19

Worksheets:
- Multiple Choice (or Not!)
- True – or Alternative Fact?
- Fever Facts
- Self-Rating Scale
- Steps You Can Take
- Action Plan
- Other Points to Remember

When an Outsider Gave Medical Orders

I n the middle of the Spanish Flu epidemic, Pastor Malcolm Mackintosh happened by the hospital room of a very sick middle-aged woman. The attending nurse was just pulling a curtain around the patient's bed when the pastor walked by.

"What's the matter?" the pastor wanted to know.

"This lady is dying," the nurse replied. "Pretty soon I'll be pulling the curtain for that one over there, too," she said, pointing to a nearby, struggling patient.

"Where's the doctor?" the pastor asked.

"What doctor?" the nurse was incredulous. "Every doctor in this place has so many patients, he can't even catch some sleep. There's no doctor to be found, anywhere. I wish I knew what to do."

Pastor Mackintosh looked at the nearly lifeless patient lying there on the bed. She truly was just about gone. Then he did something that couldn't be done in our modern world.

"Get me six blankets," he said to the nurse. When the blankets arrived, the pastor spread them all out on a nearby bed—except one. The last blanket was dipped in boiling water, then placed on top of the others and allowed to cool just a tad. With the help of two other men, he lifted the patient onto the blanketed bed. As a final step, he wrapped her up in the blankets as if she was in a cocoon.

"Leave her there for about two hours," he instructed the nurse. "Then do the exact same thing again and let her 'roast' for another two hours."

The nurse did exactly as she was told and, to the amazement of nearly all, the sick woman not only revived, but was well enough to go home in just a few days![29]

"Roasting" the Patient?

What was the treatment Pastor Mackintosh recommended when he told the nurse to let the patient "roast" for a few hours? He was simply recommending that heat—which he knew would create an artificial fever—be used. The combination of moisture with heat, as was well known in the sanitariums of those days, made the treatment much more powerful.[30] Pastor Mackintosh had learned how to do hydrotherapy treatments years earlier at a sanitarium in Colorado. There one of the doctors, noticing his unhealthy appearance, had offered to have his hydrotherapy students "train" on the good pastor. Pastor Mackintosh then took notes on the treatments he had received, learning to do them himself.

It is well-documented that virtually all animals develop a fever naturally whenever they start to get sick.[31] This response occurs because it gives them the very best chance to beat the illness that they are fighting. Similarly, when a virus comes knocking at your door, a fever is often just the remedy needed.

Benefits of a Fever

A fever performs three basic functions for the body:
- Turning up the body's heat high enough that invading organisms can't survive
- Revving the body's metabolism (which enables the body to destroy pathogens faster), and
- Stimulating the immune system.[32]

Turning Up the Heat

In its efforts to raise its temperature, the body relies on several heat-generating mechanisms to help fight off the bug. One of those is vasoconstriction. Vasoconstriction conserves blood for the vital organs by limiting blood flow to the skin. This is what makes a person pale when they have a fever.[33] Piloerection (where a person's hair stands on end), is another strategy the body employs in its efforts to produce heat.[34] Other body protection processes that launch whenever a fever begins include increases in:

- Metabolic rate (which in turn speeds up cell function)[35]
- Antibody production (antibodies are cells trained specifically to fight whatever the body is being invaded by).[36]
- White blood cell production (another way of ramping up efforts to fight off the bug)[37] and
- Interferon production. (Interferon is a natural anticancer and antiviral substance which got its name by "interfering" with the spread of invaders to healthy cells.)[38]

As a result of all this helpful activity, a fever can impair the replication of many bacteria and viruses. During the 1800's and early 1900's, many sanitariums relied on hydrotherapy as a way to fight disease by artificially raising body temperature. In recent years, an increasing number of people are recognizing the value of this simple treatment in helping the body stave off illness.

NOTE: **While creating an artificial fever is often very beneficial, there are some patients (such as infants and the elderly) for which creating a fever is not a good idea.**

New Study Highlights Water Treatment as a Potential Ally in the Fight Against COVID-19

NOTE: This section is excerpted from a press release reporting a study authored by Dr. Ramirez on the potential benefits of hydrotherapy (and hydrothermotherapy) in the war against COVID-19.

Researchers in a new study have documented how a form of water treatment, known as hydrotherapy, can significantly improve the immune system response for the fight against COVID-19. The scientists, led by Dr. Francisco (Eddie) Ramirez, believe that hydrotherapy has important implications as a treatment option during the pandemic.

Although 80% of COVID-19 cases are mild in nature, about 20% of sufferers exhibit symptoms that are markedly more severe. These 20% also face an increased risk of death. In recent months, it has become increasingly clear that an overreaction of the immune system is a primary factor impacting the severity of the illness.[39]

In a new study published in the Journal of Medical Hypotheses, Dr. Ramirez and colleagues propose that a healthier immune system, enhanced by water treatment, can reduce the risk of and/or minimize, complications associated with COVID-19.[40] Their findings are based on previous studies detailing how hydrotherapy strengthens the immune system.

Hydrotherapy (also known as hydrothermotherapy), is a time-tested intervention dating back to as early as 3000 BC. In such therapies, the combination of water (hydro) and heat (thermo) results in increased blood flow and circulation of white blood cells throughout the body. The increased circulation allows lymph fluid to move more efficiently. The end result is a stronger immune system, empowered to resist the common cold, flu, and even COVID-19 more energetically than it otherwise could have. Common hydrotherapy modalities include saunas, steam baths, Jacuzzis, sweat rooms, and fomentations.

In Finland, more than a fourth of those diagnosed with COVID-19 are "foreign language speakers" (as they are called). In addition, three fourths of the people in Finland who died from COVID were foreigners. This in spite of the fact that these non-native residents accounted for only 8% of the population. Taneli Pirskanen from Karpalo Institute in Finland, who assisted Dr. Ramirez with his study, believes that higher usage of saunas by the Finnish natives could be the reason behind this statistic.

Finnish Saunas vs. COVID-19

The habit of taking a sauna once or twice a week is widely practiced in Nordic countries, even amid COVID-related restrictions. The use of hydrotherapy as a healing modality has not been restricted to Finland, however. In Japan, the traditional Sento (public bath) and Mushi Buro (closet bath) are still widely used. The Turkish Bath (hammam), the Mesoamerican temescal, and Native American sweat lodges are all examples of hydrothermotherapy— with related benefits—still widely practiced in certain cultures today. Water treatments have also been practiced in India, with evidence of steam baths in that country dating back several thousand years.

Economical and Accessible

"One of the most encouraging aspects of hydrotherapy treatment," notes Dr. Ramirez, "is that the resources needed are readily available worldwide. The basic, essential tools are simple: water, a way to heat the water, and towels. That is enough to get you started with a potentially life-saving hydrotherapy intervention. While hydrotherapy shouldn't be the only strategy for preventing or treating COVID, it can strongly complement many other interventions."

Lessons From the 1918 Pandemic (H1N1 Virus)

During the Spanish Flu pandemic of 1918, a network of health centers known as "sanitariums" treated the flu using evidence-based interventions that included hydrotherapy. During that pandemic, mortality in the public hospitals ranged between 13 and 40%. In military hospitals, where better treatment modalities were available, the mortality rate was still 6.7%. Neither of these treatment providers were using hydrotherapy. In contrast, in sanitariums where hydrotherapy was used, mortality rates ranged from 1.3% (for inpatients) to 3.8% (for outpatients). This significant difference in outcomes when hydrotherapy was used deserves renewed attention in light of the current pandemic.[41]

Research Continues

In addition to a review of literature documenting how hydrotherapy boosts the immune system, Dr. Ramirez and his colleagues are also involved in a practical clinical trial.

"The clinical trial is the second part of this study," confirms Dr. Ramirez. "In this trial, a group of COVID-19 hospital patients in California have been treated with hydrotherapy. The response of these patients is then analyzed through the use of several blood tests. The preliminary results are very encouraging, as not a single patient treated with hydrotherapy experienced severe COVID-19 symptoms. As a result, hospitalizations were avoided."[42]

Multiple Choice (or Not!)

After reviewing the chapter assignments, circle the correct answer(s) for each of the questions below. (Note – some questions have more than one right answer.)

1. The heat from a fever in the body:
   a. Makes it much harder for germs to survive
   b. Ramps up white blood cell, antibody, and interferon production
   c. Is nature's way of fighting off an infection
   d. All of the above

2. Letting a fever run can:
   a. Lengthen the time of an illness
   b. Shorten the time of an illness
   c. Result in extreme abdominal pain
   d. Make the sufferer more infectious to others

3. Historically, physicians have noticed that a fever could have a beneficial effect on the conditions of:
   a. Epilepsy
   b. Depression
   c. Insanity
   d. All of the above

4. Vasoconstriction is a bodily defense mechanism that:
   a. Restricts blood flow to the skin
   b. Sends more blood flow to the skin
   c. Conserves blood flood flow for the vital organs
   d. Makes a sick person look pale

5. Artificial fever therapy:
   a. Stimulates the immune system
   b. Improves blood circulation
   c. Helps eliminate toxins
   d. Promotes better and deeper sleep

6. Fever meds aren't ideal as a treatment because they:
   a. Mask the symptoms of illness without treating the underlying cause
   b. Make the illness more contagious to others
   c. May lengthen the time of illness
   d. All of the above

7. When a fever is very high and can't be brought down by natural means, the sick person should:
   a. Take the "Ice Bucket" challenge
   b. Soak in a hot tub
   c. Drink more lemonade
   d. Seek immediate medical attention

8. Hyperthermia is:
   a. A dangerous condition caused by overexposure to moisture and cold
   b. An up-and-coming treatment that kills cancer cells
   c. A state of profuse (hyper) sweating on a very hot day
   d. Not recommended under any circumstances

9. The Finnish people:
   a. Own more saunas per capita than any other culture
   b. Have done many important things in saunas (including but not limited to being born and negotiating political treaties)
   c. View the sauna as the "Poor Man's Pharmacy," capable of healing many ills
   d. All of the above

10. People who get less than 7 hours of sleep per night:
   a. Run a greater risk of infection
   b. Are more likely to die prematurely
   c. Run a greater risk of depression
   d. All the above

11. Benefits of hydrotherapy include:
   a. Improved blood circulation and immune system function
   b. Soothing of sore muscles and pain relief overall
   c. Detoxification and faster metabolism
   d. The ability to eat more food in less time

12. Researchers in the Netherlands have found that "polar bear plunges":
   a. Triggers major changes in oxygen and CO2 levels which are beneficial to immune system function
   b. Are highly effective as a punishment to deter petty theft
   c. Send a rush of adrenaline to the body which inhibits inflammatory response
   d. Are only helpful when a cold Nordic lake is involved

True – or Alternative Fact?

Circle the correct True or False answer for each of the statements below:

1.	The high heat and low humidity in a typical hydrotherapy treatment causes blood vessels to dilate, resulting in improved heart function.	True	False
2.	In order to truly benefit from hydrotherapy, you must own or at least have access to an expensive sauna.	True	False
3.	Hot and cold showers are an inexpensive, highly available, and often effective form of hydrotherapy.	True	False
4.	Moist heat has been found to penetrate the body 27 times more effectively than dry.	True	False
5.	The shock of a contrast (hot to cold) hydrotherapy treatment should be avoided by persons who are frail, elderly, or suffer from heart problems or arrhythmia	True	False
6.	Stay-at-home orders and working from home have nothing to do with circadian rhythm.	True	False
7.	A walk-in freezer (or other very cold room) is an ideal place to do hydrotherapy.	True	False
8.	Drinking warm water enhances blood circulation by breaking down fat deposits in the blood.	True	False
9.	Drinking warm water in the morning clogs the system.	True	False
10.	Low and high core body temperatures are both dangerous.	True	False

Fever Facts

Match up the fever ranges with the action you should take for each one:

Low Temperature	Uh oh. Time to slow down and get some rest!
Normal Temperature	Time to check in with your doc!
Light Fever	Call the ambulance! You're going to the Emergency Room!
Moderate Fever	Rest a lot! Try to bring the temp down through natural means. If you can't bring it down within 24 hours, seek medical help.
High Fever	Rest in earnest. Keep a careful eye on that temp. If it goes on for three or more days, seek medical help.
Very High Fever	You're "fit as a fiddle" – or at least your temperature is.

SESSION 2 / Worksheets
Self-Rating Scale
INSTRUCTIONS: Circle the answer that fits you best.

	😀	😐	🙁	😢
Whenever I start running a fever, I:	Rest and drink lots of water	Slow down just a tad	Go full speed ahead	Take over-the-counter meds right away
If I or someone under my care starts to run a fever, I:	Have a good plan in place	Have a plan, but it's not in place	Fly by the seat of my pants	Have no idea what to do
When trying to fight off an infection, I automatically think of:	Hydrotherapy methods	Trying not to infect others	What over-the-counter med might help me	Getting to a walk-in clinic ASAP
I have some form of hydrotherapy readily available in my home and know how to use it:	Of course!	Working on it...	Do I have to answer that question?	Not a chance!
I am aware of some natural ways to lower a fever:	Yes!	Possibly	What are you talking about?	Why would I want to do that?
I drink a few glasses of warm water every morning shortly after waking:	Always	Most of the time	Sometimes	No.
My urine color is usually pale, indicating that I am well hydrated:	Always	Most of the time	Sometimes	Not!
Drinking water is an important part of my daily routine:	Always	Most of the time	Sometimes	Not exactly!
When fighting an infection, one of the first things I do is stop eating sugar:	Absolutely!	Sometimes	Not as much as I should	Not really

Review your answers in the previous section. Are there any simple and/or immediate steps you can take to improve in any of these areas? If so, list them below:

Steps I Can Take:

1 _____

_____

_____

2 _____

_____

_____

3 _____

_____

_____

4 _____

_____

_____

5 _____

_____

_____

_____

Action Plan

Review the "Action Plan" from chapters 3 and 4 as summarized below. Put a check mark by the ones you are ready to work on:

- ◯ The next time you start to run a fever, think twice before taking over-the-counter medications.

- ◯ Familiarize yourself with non-drug ways to lower a fever, and have the needed supplies on hand.

- ◯ Consider ways that you can raise your body temperature to fight an infection, and have any needed supplies on hand.

- ◯ Look around your home and take note of what you have that could be used for hydrotherapy and make a plan for how you would use it.

- ◯ Do a "trial run" of the hydrotherapy treatment of your choice. To boost the immune system and improve overall health, consider engaging in this hydrotherapy regularly, whether you are sick or not.

- ◯ Consider how much water you are (or aren't) drinking. If you aren't drinking enough, think of and implement some "micro habits" that will help you to drink more water as part of your daily routine.

Other Points to Remember

Are there other points you would like to remember from the chapters covered in this session? If so, write them here:

_____

_____

_____

_____

_____

_____

_____

Reading Assignments:
Chapter 5: Breathe to Heal: The Secret of Forest Bathing
Chapter 6: Guard Your Nose: And Entire Respiratory Tract

What You'll Learn:
At the end of this session, you will have a better understanding of:

Chapter 5:
- What "forest bathing" is, why it's so very popular in Japan, and how to do it
- The special health-promoting secrets of certain trees, and how you can benefit
- The immune-boosting superpowers of pure, fresh air
- How negative ions promote health, and the easiest way to breathe some daily

Chapter 6:
- The major role of the nose and respiratory tract in the growth and spread of viruses and infections (including COVID-19)
- The role of your "sniffer" in tasting, and how that's connected to taste buds down in your lungs
- The perils of constant mouth breathing
- How your lungs work to shield and protect your body
- The GERD (Gastrointestinal Reflux Disease) / lung disease connection
- Best tips for lung care

Bonus Sections:
- The Nose-Brain Connection
- How Posture Impacts Breathing and Overall Health

Worksheets:
- Multiple Choice (or Not!)
- True – or Alternative Fact?
- Stats to Remember
- Self-Rating Scale
- Steps You Can Take
- Action Plan
- Other Points to Remember

The Nose-Brain Connection

"**M**y sense of smell isn't working!" those words have been spoken all too frequently by those afflicted with the Delta (though not the Omicron) COVID variant.[43] To many, the loss of smell has been a passing inconvenience. For others, the disabled "sniffer" has lingered far beyond other symptoms.[44] In addition to those who have lost their sense of smell through COVID, there are those who can't smell very well due to sinus congestion or other difficulties.

Many people consider losing the sense of smell to be quite inconvenient. Being unable to "smell the roses" removes some joy from their lives. But does the sense of smell really matter or impact health? Researchers say that it does!

Recent studies have highlighted a strong connection between mental health and how well a person can smell. In one study, researchers checked the "sniffers" of more than 2,900 adults aged 57-85 to see how well they could detect five different smells: fish, leather, peppermint, orange, and rose.

When the scientists followed up with study participants five years later, they found that those who couldn't identify at least four of the five odors in the initial test were more than twice as likely to have developed dementia.[45]

In another study, researchers found that the lower a subject's ability to smell an orange, the greater the odds of having dementia.[46] The breakdown in brain function related to loss of smell is likely related to the close connection of the olfactory glands to core brain functions such as emotion, memory, and pleasure. In addition to dementia, a less-than-optimal nasal microbiome has been linked to the development of asthma and other health challenges.[47]

Why Your Nose is at Risk

Like the mouth and the gut, the nose has a collection of bacteria and other microbes of its own. When not adequately protected, your nose may (simply by "sitting out there" and sampling air) provides a straight path to the brain for harmful substances. Despite the hazards of being "out there," the nose is still the best way to breathe. Researchers have found that inhaling through the nose not only stimulates the brain, but boosts memory as well.[48]

The nasal microbiome, like the other microbiomes in your body, is crucial to overall health.[49] This means you need to watch out for "bad guy" microbes in the nose just as you would in the mouth, gut, or other areas of the body that house a microbiome. Researchers have found that enemy microbes, once in the nose, can climb the olfactory nerve. As they work their way farther into the body (and nearer the brain), these "bad guys" trigger inflammation and with it, dementia.[50] In addition, scientists have found that people with more good bacteria in their nasal passages are at much lower risk of certain respiratory issues. Lactobacillus (a bacteria which has antimicrobial and anti-inflammatory properties) was found to be about 10 times more plentiful in the noses of healthy people than in those with chronic nasal and sinus inflammation.[51]

Researchers believe the good bacteria in the nose promotes immune system function providing a barrier to invaders, fighting pathogens, reducing inflammation, and balancing things out overall. More studies are needed, but these potential mechanisms suggest that a healthy nasal microbiome may act as a first line of defense by:

- Tackling viruses before they gain a foothold in the body
- Warding off bacteria that could lead to sinus infections, and
- Protecting against the inhalation of pollen, mold, and other allergens.

Factors that negatively impact the nasal microbiome include smoking, overuse of antibiotics, and poor gut health.[52]

How to Strengthen Your Nasal Microbiome

There's no magic bullet for improving the health of your nasal microbiome. However, there are some protective steps you can take:

- Try a probiotic nasal spray, which can help balance the microbiome of your nose.[53]
- Avoid antibiotics (which ideally would be prescribed following evidence-based guidelines after a culture is taken.)
- Avoid smoking and breathing second-hand smoke.[54]

Good News for Recovery

For those who lost their smell due to COVID-19, there is some good news. Researchers have found that, in most coronavirus cases, it was inflammation of the olfactory nerve that caused the loss of smell. Rather than being permanently damaged, the nerve was inflamed. As the inflammation subsides, the sense of smell should return.[55]

An Important Warning

The loss of smell experienced by many during the recent pandemic has alerted many people to the importance of the often-forgotten function of their "sniffer." Recent studies highlighting the connection between the ability to smell and other brain function (among other health concerns) should also be a "warning shot over the bow." The loss of the sense of smell should not be taken lightly. If your nose doesn't detect various smells as you think it should, that could be a signal that some other health issue is going on—an issue you need to sleuth out and address before it becomes life-changing in a negative way.

How Posture Affects Breathing and Overall Health

If you haven't heard of "text neck" yet, you probably will very soon. A growing number of young people are developing the same "forward head posture" that has afflicted computer users and other desk workers for decades. All too often, the result of all this sedentary straining is a literal pain in the neck, jaw, or shoulder (not to mention headaches and spinal challenges).[56] While the focus is often on the pain associated with poor posture, the way we breathe when we slouch plays an important role in overall health and immune system function as well.[57]

Simply put, good posture helps your body to breathe—and function—better. When you slouch (especially when seated), the body compresses the thoracic region so that the diaphragm can't open fully when breathing. Poor posture prevents your diaphragm from efficiently expanding your chest and lungs, with diminished breathing capacity being the inevitable result.[58] Over time, the reduced lung capacity that results from slouching can leave you short of breath, or at the very minimum, make you tire more easily. Soon, basic activities (such as climbing stairs) become an exhausting endeavor. By changing your center of gravity, poor posture also increases your risk of a bone-breaking fall.[59]

The Dangers of Shallow Breathing

Its normal for both humans and animals to take shallow breaths when feeling anxious, nervous, or threatened. Whenever a shallow breath is taken, the body over-breathes oxygen and expels too much carbon dioxide. By keeping the nervous system in a state of high alert, shallow breathing alters blood chemistry in a negative way. The body responds to continued shallow breathing by setting new thresholds for carbon dioxide in the arterial receptors, which then stimulate the body to breathe faster than required. As a result, the continued increase in carbon dioxide levels triggers an ongoing shortness of breath sensation.[60]

Posture Influences Everything

The negative implications of poor posture (and long-term shallow breathing) to overall health include:

- A weakened immune system[61]
- High blood pressure[62]
- Insomnia[63]
- Respiratory problems[64]
- Stress-related illnesses[65]

In addition to the physical impact, poor posture brings social and psychological implications. People who are stressed or depressed don't sit with straight backs and open shoulders or walk with confidence. With hunched backs and rounded shoulders, they tend to gaze towards the floor and have a gloomy overall outlook on life. Their poor posture is impacting their mood and emotions, which affects their health.[66] This alters their breathing pattern, which impacts their posture again, continuing the unhealthy cycle.

Good News for Slouchers!

If you have a lifelong habit of slouching, there is still good news. By improving your posture, you can break the unhealthy cycle, improve your emotional health, and make it easier for your optimal breathing muscle (the diaphragm) to work efficiently and well.

Researchers have found that exercise and activating the deep muscles of the body can significantly improve both its alignment and breathing capacity.[67] Because the body isn't used to taking in sufficient air, positive change can be difficult at first. With practice, however, poor posture (and the accompanying bad breathing habits) can be improved. Even small changes in posture can make a positive impact on physical and emotional health.[68]

Ways to Improve Posture and Breathing

1. Take regular breaks. Even small movements, done frequently, can help to reset the postural muscles.

2. Have a technology holiday! (e.g. dump the phone!) If you can't do that because of your job, consider taking breaks during the day. Or get a larger phone with better ergonomics and/or bigger, easy-to-read letters.

3. Stretch your body! Exercises like the cat-cow, chin-tuck, and downward dog are great for loosening overworked muscles.

4. Try a standing desk when working, or at the least, an ergonomically helpful chair.

5. Set an alarm to go off every 30 minutes and re-set your posture each time it rings. Do this until good posture (and breathing) becomes a habit.

6. Find some good breathing exercises and do them. Daily!

7. When feeling stressed, repeat the little rhyme "Without fail, exhale!" And then do it!

Multiple Choice (or Not!)

After reviewing the chapter assignments, circle the correct answer(s) for each of the questions below. (Note – some questions have more than one right answer.)

1. In Japan, forest bathing has become popular as a natural remedy for:
a. Scoliosis
b. Stress management
c. Plantar's Warts
d. None of the above

2. The "secret of the trees" seems to lie in the higher oxygen content in forests coupled with fungus, insect, and bacteria-fighting plant chemicals known as:
a. Chlorokyll
b. Stemnovores
c. Phytoncides
d. Negative ions

3. Tree varieties that have been shown to emit the highest levels of healthy chemicals include:
a. Evergreens such as pine, cedar, spruce, eucalyptus, and conifers
b. Maple trees (especially Red Maples)
c. Japanese White Birch, Himalayan Birch, and Betula Nana trees
d. Ornamental shrubs (including Lilacs and Burning Bushes)

4. Forest bathing has been scientifically shown to boost health and well-being by:
a. Improving immune system function
b. Promoting better sleep patterns
c. Improving metabolic and cardiovascular health
d. Reducing stress, depression, anxiety and/or anger

5. During World War I, casualties who were treated in open air hospitals:
a. Got the chills
b. Often contracted pneumonia
c. Had better survival rates
d. Drank bone broth to stay warm

6. Scientists have found that children who grow up near "green spaces" are less likely, later in life, to:
a. Suffer from anxiety or depression
b. Develop a psychiatric illness later
c. Become an alcoholic
d. All of the above

7. Beneficial negative ions can be found:
a. Floating around in nature (especially near waterfalls, mountains, forests, and oceans)
b. Right in your bathroom shower
c. Emanating from high-powered air conditioning systems
d. Near well-maintained sewage lagoons

8. The human nose is a major infection point for the transmission of:
a. Harmful bacteria in the stomach
b. AIDS
c. Colds, the flu, and viruses such as COVID-19
d. All of the above

9. Because of its role as an air filter (removing harmful dirt and germs before the air goes into the lungs), the nose is:
a. One of the dirtiest organs of the body
b. Kept busy accumulating and wrapping up waste in the form of mucus
c. Taboo as a topic among the royalty of Morocco
d. More effective if longer

10. In addition to being found in your mouth, human taste buds (which play an important role in immune system function) are also found in your:
a. Heart
b. Lungs
c. Anterior ligament muscles
d. Nose

11. Challenges with mouth breathing include:
a. Intake of unfiltered, unprocessed air
b. Dry mouth
c. Bad breath and inflammation of the gums
d. All of the above

12. Important functions of the lungs include:
a. Working closely with the heart to help it function more efficiently
b. Filtering out small blood clots as well as air bubbles
c. Protecting against excess carbon dioxide in the body
d. Fighting infection through the secretion of immunoglobulin

True – or Alternative Fact?

Circle the correct True or False answer for each of the statements below:

1.	Smoking causes 90% of all lung cancer deaths.	True	False
2.	Because smoking impairs lung function, smokers are more vulnerable to respiratory illnesses such as pneumonia and COVID-19.	True	False
3.	Environmental pollutants such as artificial fragrances, perfumes, chemical fumes, dust and/or mold are easily filtered out by the lungs.	True	False
4.	A regular exercise program can help the body to get more oxygen into the bloodstream.	True	False
5.	Acid reflux and lung disease symptoms are totally unrelated.	True	False
6.	Eating acidic foods, excessive salt, fried foods, cold cuts, and dairy products can make it more difficult to breathe.	True	False
7.	COVID-19 never impacts the long-term health of the lungs.	True	False
8.	Scientists have discovered a strong connection between IPF (Idiopathic Pulmonary Fibrosis) and GERD (Gastrointestinal Reflux Disease).	True	False
9.	People who take a walk in the forest during the day tend to sleep better at night.	True	False
10.	Forest bathing has been found to have a negative effect on adiponectin (a protein that helps regulate blood sugar levels).	True	False

Stats to Remember

Match each phrase on the left to the figure that best fits it on the right.

Number of gallons of air you inhale every day	15
Percentage of time that the average person spends indoors	1,500
Number of times per minute a human normally breathes	90%
Percentage of lung cancer patients who die as a result of smoking	22,000
Average number of breaths a person takes each day	2,000

Self-Rating Scale

INSTRUCTIONS: Circle the answer that fits you best.

	😊	😐	😟	😢
My sense of smell is really quite sharp:	Of course!	Could use some improvement	Definitely lacking	What sense of smell?
I get out in the fresh air each day:	Always	Frequently	Once in a while	Never
I struggle with acid reflux:	Not a problem at all	Only rarely	Most of the time	It's the bane of my existence!
I often spend time among the trees or in other green spaces:	Of course!	Frequently	Not as much as I should	Never
I have chronic sinus congestion:	All the time	Quite a bit	Once in a while	Hardly ever
I tend to breathe through my nose:	Always	Most of the time	Sometimes	Not at all
Except for during extreme exercise, I rarely get short of breath:	That would be correct!	That's not totally true	I'm frequently out of breath	Getting enough air is a real challenge for me
My diet is rich in foods that are good for my lungs:	Always	Most of the time	Once in a while	Not exactly!
I smoke or breathe second-hand smoke:	Never	Once in a while	Much of the time	Without fail!

Review your answers in the previous section. Are there any simple and/or immediate steps you can take to improve in any of these areas? If so, list them below:

Steps I Can Take:

1 _____

_____

_____

_____

2 _____

_____

_____

_____

3 _____

_____

_____

_____

4 _____

_____

_____

_____

5 _____

_____

_____

_____

Action Plan

**Review the "Action Plan" from chapters 5 and 6 as summarized below.
Put a check mark by the ones you are ready to work on:**

- ○ Think about the percentage of time you spend indoors and out. Are you struggling with "Nature Deficit Disorder"? If so, consider ways that might be changed.

- ○ Make a list of ways that you could be exposed to more ions, and decide how to get started.

- ○ Open your windows for 10-20 minutes daily to let the fresh air in (unless you live in a very smoggy place).

- ○ Make a resolution to get outside for some light exercise and fresh air at least several times daily.

- ○ If you have "lived with" a chronic sinus infection, try considering that in a new light. Do you really want a virtual virus factory living inside your nose?

- ○ Taking the suggestions made in these chapters, make and implement a plan to improve the health of your nose and entire respiratory tract.

- ○ If you have frequent acid reflux, or are a habitual mouth breather, give some thought as to how you can improve your habits in those areas.

Other Points to Remember

Are there other points you would like to remember from the chapters covered in this session? If so, write them here:

_____

_____

_____

_____

_____

_____

Reading Assignments:
Chapter 7: Heal Your Gut: Microbes Are Your Friend
Chapter 18: Brush Your Teeth: The Dental-Immune System Link

What You'll Learn:
At the end of this session, you will have a better understanding of:

Chapter 7:
- The bacterial battle raging within your body
- The critical relationship between your gut and immune system health
- Why your gut is most like that of your mother and siblings
- Gut health "weak spots" to watch out for
- What to eat – and not eat – to promote a healthier gut

Chapter 18:
- The startling connection between gum disease and diseases (including COVID-19)
- The role of gingivitis as a trigger point for disease
- How "mask mouth" promotes poor health, and how to avoid it – even if wearing a mask
- The incredibly close mouth-gut connection – and its role in immune system function
- The dire health results of gum disease, and how to avoid them
- Why most mouthwashes aren't the answer
- Chemicals to watch out for in oral health products

Bonus Sections:
- Eating the Rainbow
- Microbes – Your New BFFs

Worksheets:
- Multiple Choice (or Not!)
- True – or Alternative Fact?
- Meaningful Matching
- Self-Rating Scale
- Steps You Can Take
- Action Plan
- Other Points to Remember

Eating the Rainbow

Dr. Terry Wahls used to climb mountains in Nepal and run marathons. She competed in long distance cross-country ski events, earned a black belt in taekwondo, and even won a bronze medal in the 1978 Pan American Games. Then her world fell apart. She was diagnosed with multiple sclerosis.

After her diagnosis, Dr. Wahl's health — and ability to do things — declined rapidly. Despite seeking out the best medical advice and following it carefully, she found herself confined to a wheelchair within three years. She was 52 years old at the time.

An avid researcher, Dr. Wahl decided to study things out for herself. Recognizing the connection between nutrition and health, she became fascinated with supplements and what they might do for her health. Based on her research, Dr. Wahl developed a list of supplements she felt would benefit her. She reviewed the list of with her doctor, who felt they would be safe to try.

After two months of supplementation Dr. Wahl became discouraged and stopped. She wasn't getting better, so why bother? She was surprised to find that, two days after stopping the supplements, she couldn't even get out of bed. The supplements hadn't healed her, but they were apparently doing something positive for her health!

With renewed energy, Dr. Wahl dived back into her nutritional research. When she came across the topic of lifestyle medicine, she began to wonder if the nutrients she was deriving from supplements couldn't be obtained from diet instead. The best way to get this nutrition, Dr. Wahl believed, was through a whole food nutrient-targeted eating plan. (The connection between diet and M.S. was first discovered and documented by Dr. Roy Swank, who spent his entire career studying and documenting that connection.[69])

It took time, but as she altered her diet, Dr. Wahl managed to do much more than arrest her disease. Her stunning results included a dramatic restoration of both function and health.[70] The protocol she followed, and later recommended to others, was simple. Known as the "9-cup Diet," it involved eating three cups each per day of:

- **LEAFY GREENS** (cooked or raw)
- **DEEPLY COLORED** fruits and veggies
- **SULFUR-RICH VEGGIES** (such as onions, cabbage, garlic, broccoli, kale, cauliflower, etc.)

The 9-cup diet protocol Dr. Wahl used with such success can be broken down into an even simpler formula. It's called "eating the rainbow." A quick look at the list of fruits and veggies in the 9-cup plan (which can be reduced to 6 cups for smaller people) reveals a wide spectrum — or rainbow — of colors.

Colorful Fruits & Veggies (examples below):

- **GREEN:** avocadoes, celery, cucumbers, green pepper, kiwi, zucchini
- **RED:** beets, cherries, pomegranates, raspberries, red cabbage, red peppers, strawberries
- **BLUE/PURPLE/BLACK:** blackberries, black olives, black or purple grapes, blueberries, prunes, purple kale
- **YELLOW/ORANGE:** carrots, grapefruit, lemons, mangos, oranges, pumpkin, squash, sweet potatoes, yams

A Good Goal to Have

If you're like many people, you tend to focus on eating the foods you like. There are challenges with a narrow diet, however. When we focus on just a few foods, we miss out on the host of health benefits that comes from eating a wide variety of veggies and fruits. When your dietary choices are narrow, the range of bacteria in your gut becomes very narrow as well.[71]

People in the rural areas of the world that have low rates of all kinds of diseases have a much wider range of "bugs" in the gut than the average American.[72] They might eat a lot of bananas, but they also might have 30 varieties of that one fruit. One of the key secrets behind their lower disease rates — and longevity — is the colorful diet they eat.[73]

Nature has tried to make things easy for us by "color coding" veggies and fruits. The different colors relate to the vitamins, minerals, and phytochemicals in each. Our bodies need this variety of nutrients, which is why "eating the rainbow" is such a fundamentally healthy way of life!

To get more color in your diet, a good goal would be to eat two servings of each color of food each day. By getting a variety of color in your diet, you're giving your body an array of vitamins, minerals, and phytochemicals to benefit your health. Your gut health will also be better if you try new things.

Tips for Getting Out of Your Food Comfort Zone

- The next time you go to the grocery store, try something new! In the produce aisle, look for fruits and veggies you aren't familiar with.
- Check the Internet for some new recipes.
- As you are working to eat more of the rainbow, watch for high fiber options as well. A high fiber diet, like a colorful one, is very beneficial to the gut.

A diet high in processed foods is naturally deficient in the colorful micronutrients needed for healthy bodies.[74] Because there are more than 3,000 micronutrients needed by the body, they simply can't be gotten through a pill.[75] Rather, the best health-boosting strategy is to eat a rainbow-colored plant-based high fiber diet.

Microbes: Your New BFFs

In case you haven't heard, "BFF" is a common acronym for "Best Friends Forever." While mostly used in a social setting, BFF also describes the type of relationship your body needs to have with the healthy microbes sharing its space.

In the book Pandemic Busters, we highlighted the close relationship between gut health and immune system function. In addition to boosting the body's defenses, gut health also deeply impacts the inflammation level within the body and its various organs.[76]

How things Work

When we eat foods that feed bad gut bacteria (such as highly processed, greasy, or sugary foods), the bad gut bacteria irritate the body. Inflammation sets in when the body rushes blood to the irritated areas in response.[77] That's why inflammation, which has been implicated as a causal factor in so many diseases, is often related to imbalances that start in the gut. These imbalances emerge when the bad bugs outnumber, and even overwhelm, the good. Some unhealthy microbes have themselves been directly tied to disease. For example, researchers have linked Streptococcus bovis (an unhealthy microbe) directly to colon cancer.[78]

The Challenge with Dietary Improvements

While many people want to eat healthier, not many carry through to make long-lasting changes. One of the reasons for the frequent failures, despite the best of intentions, is the action of "bad bugs" in the gut.

The microbes living in your gut are in the habit of sending signals to your brain. They do this through the vagus nerve, which connects the gut (among other organs) directly to the brain.[79]

When you stop eating junk food, you effectively stop feeding the unhealthy microbes residing in your gut. As the bad microbes become hungry, they send their complaints to the brain. It's a natural "bug-jerk" reaction, since the bad microbes want to live.

This is why we often don't feel well when we change our diet for the better. "Bad guy" microbes start making a fuss in the gut, and pretty soon we are thinking, "oh, this diet doesn't work for me. It makes me feel bad."

Mind Over Microbes

This is a case where "mind over matter," or microbes (in this situation) is really important. The good news is that, as you stop feeding the unhealthy microbes, they will start to die off and the good guys will regain control.

Like the "bad guys," healthy bacteria can also send signals of satisfaction to the brain. As the balance of good versus bad bacteria begins to change in your gut, your brain will eventually get signals that you are indeed feeling better.[80]

In recent years, researchers have reported that gut bacteria influences our moods. People with a high diversity of good gut bacteria tend to have better mental health.[81] In contrast, a low diversity of gut bacteria is linked to depression.[82]

When unhealthy bacteria gain control of the gut (an imbalance known as dysbiosis), inflammation begins to set in.[83] The inflammation widens the space between each cell (a process known as bacterial translocation). When this happens, bacteria travels to — and infects — places in the body where it should not be. This inevitable result (known in medical circles as increased intestinal permeability) is often called "leaky gut syndrome."[84]

People suffering from leaky gut syndrome often visit their medical professional. Sometimes medications are prescribed. Unfortunately, medications often exacerbate the problem. Soon the patient is locked in a vicious cycle: more medications, followed by feeling worse, followed by even more medications.

Bacterial Poverty

It's been said that when we gain wealth, we lose bacteria. This is true. This pattern has been repeated all over the world. The more money people make the more likely they are to choose unhealthy foods.[85] As the bad bacteria thrive, good bacteria are lost. It doesn't have to be that way, however.

The next time you decide what to eat for a meal, think of the poorest people of the world. The people who eat a lot of fruits, veggies, rice, and beans. Then try to eat more like them — and put a lot of color on your plate as well. The bad bacteria in your gut might send sour-bug SOS signals up your vagus nerve for a while. But once you've adjusted, your gut (and entire body) will thank you for making the change!

Multiple Choice (or Not!)

After reviewing the chapter assignments, circle the correct answer(s) for each of the questions below. (Note – some questions have more than one right answer.)

1. The number of organisms living in your gut is:
 a. 3-4 million
 b. A gazillion billion
 c. About 40 trillion
 d. 11,523 on a good day

2. The microbiome, or mini-ecosystem living in your gut, is most similar to that of your:
 a. Mother
 b. Father
 c. Siblings
 d. Paternal great uncle

3. An inoculation of microbiota are transferred to children:
 a. As they travel through the birth canal
 b. By household pets
 c. Through parental kisses
 d. All of the above

4. The makeup and diversity of your microbiome has a huge impact on the function of your:
 a. Brain
 b. Immune system
 c. Percentage of body fat
 d. Overall health and well-being

5. Foods that good gut bacteria especially love to feast on include:
 a. Salads and greens
 b. Custard-filled donuts
 c. High-fiber foods such as beans
 d. Deep-fried lard chips

6. The average American gets 60% of their calories from:
 a. Fruits and veggies
 b. Processed foods
 c. Cheese and other dairy products
 d. Sugar and pop

7. The best diet for a healthy gut includes:
 a. Diversity in food choices and colors
 b. Plant-based whole foods
 c. High-fiber foods
 d. All of the above

8. The "Dirty Dozen" are:
 a. Foods you should buy organically whenever possible
 b. Grungy root vegetables that disrupt the digestive system by clinging to molecular particles of dirt
 c. A set of fresh food choices most likely to be laden with pesticides
 d. The twelve most dangerous pesticides

9. Specific food choices that promote healthy gut bacteria include:
 a. Bananas, blueberries, and beans
 b. Cruciferous veggies such as broccoli
 c. Plant-based yogurt and tempeh
 d. All of the above

10. The microbiome of the mouth and gut:
 a. Are quite closely related
 b. Are totally unrelated
 c. Have a significant impact on overall health
 d. Are improved by smoking and/or vaping

11. Inflammation of the gums:
 a. Is a sure sign of inflammation elsewhere in the body
 b. Can lead to respiratory infections
 c. May trigger cardiovascular problems
 d. May worsen due to frequent mask wearing

12 Health challenges linked to unhealthy gums include:
 a. Anxiety and depression
 b. Cirrhosis of the liver
 c. Obesity and osteoporosis
 d. All of the above

True – or Alternative Fact?

Circle the correct True or False answer for each of the statements below:

1.	Researchers have found that people with advanced gum disease who contracted COVID-19 were much likelier to end up in Intensive Care, on a ventilator, or dead.	True	False
2.	Gingivitis is a warning sign, that if left unheeded, may be the starting point of inflammation and disease in other parts of the body.	True	False
3.	Less than 5% of the world's population suffers from gum disease.	True	False
4.	Gum disease has no relationship at all to respiratory illness.	True	False
5.	Wearing a mask may result in shallower mouth breathing, dehydration, and the breathing of recycled air.	True	False
6.	Like the gut and nose, the mouth is a bacterial playground.	True	False
7.	Only 10% of the bacteria found in the mouth are also found in the gut.	True	False
8.	Men with gum disease are much more likely to get blood cancer, kidney cancer, or pancreatic cancer.	True	False
9.	Many mouthwashes contain alcohol--an ingredient which is known to increase the risk of cancer.	True	False
10.	The avoidance of smoking is one way to improve dental health.	True	False

Meaningful Matching

Match the phrase on the left with the term(s) that best fits it to the right:

Causes of gum disease	**Aging**
	Tender gums
Gum disease symptoms	**Gut cancer**
	Heart disease
Ailments Linked to Gum Disease	**Medications**
	Receding gums

Self-Rating Scale

INSTRUCTIONS: Circle the answer that fits you best.

	😄	😐	🙁	😢
I eat a lot of sugary foods. You might say I can't get enough of them!	Not at all	Rarely	Some of the time	All the time!
Most of my diet is from unrefined whole foods.	Of course!	Usually	Once in a while	That's a joke!
I love fried foods, and eat them whenever I can.	No	Rarely	Sometimes	Every day in every way!
My diet is high in animal products such as meat, eggs, cheese, and milk.	Not at all	Once in a while	Most of the time	Always
My level of alcohol consumption is:	Non-existent	Occasional	Somewhat of a problem	A major challenge
Without my morning coffee I get a headache.	What coffee?	I can take it or leave it	Sometimes	Without fail!
My gums are sore and bleed a lot. I think I have gingivitis.	Not at all	I need to watch this	This is a definite challenge!	This is a major problem for me
Overall, I think that my oral microbiome is quite healthy.	Definitely yes	Keeping an eye on that!	Not so much	That's my Achilles heel
I am taking positive steps to improve my dental health, and feel I know what to do.	Absolutely	That's questionable	Not so sure about that	Not at all

Review your answers in the previous section. Are there any simple and/or immediate steps you can take to improve in any of these areas? If so, list them below:

Steps I Can Take:

1 _____

_____

_____

2 _____

_____

_____

3 _____

_____

_____

4 _____

_____

_____

5 _____

_____

_____

Action Plan

Review the "Action Plan" from chapters 7 and 18 as summarized below. Put a check mark by the ones you are ready to work on:

- ◯ Consider the health of your gut and whether it can be improved or not.

- ◯ Review Chapter 7 and make a list of diet changes you would like to make to improve gut health.

- ◯ Plan how you can put those changes into action, and get started.

- ◯ Understand the direct link between the health of your mouth and your body, and take the steps necessary to improve and maintain a thriving set of good bacteria in your mouth.

- ◯ If you find yourself in situations where you must wear masks for extended periods of time, do everything you can in other areas to promote good oral health.

- ◯ Review the causes of gum disease and work to improve those you have control over.

- ◯ Consider your daily dental care routine to see if there is room for improvement, and make the necessary changes.

- ◯ Review the ingredients in any toothpaste, mouthwash, or other dental products you are using, and throw out those that are harmful.

- ◯ If there is a toothache or infection in your mouth which you haven't been able to stop, visit a dentist ASAP. Taking pain killers while the infection persists allows bad bacteria to gain a stronger foothold in your body.

- ◯ Visit the dentist at least two times per year whether you have a toothache or not. A good dental cleaning will remove any plaque (bacteria) buildup on your teeth.

Other Points to Remember

Are there other points you would like to remember from the chapters covered in this session? If so, write them here:

_____

_____

_____

_____

Chapter Assignments:
Chapter 8: Diet No-Go's in Pandemic Times
Chapter 14: Cry Fowl: Chicken Soup is Not Good for Your Soul
Chapter 15: Purge Your Palate: Of Pangolins, Primates, and Penguins

What You'll Learn:
At the end of this session, you will have a better understanding of:

Chapter 8:
- Why "giving up something" is such a powerful immune-building tool
- 8 "Diet No-Go's" to consider giving up (or at least postponing) during pandemic times

Chapter 14:
- How farming has changed over the last century
- Why meat from chickens and other animals raised on factory farms poses a threat to your health
- Why chicken farms are a leading incubator for strains of avian flu, and the "super threat" of such flus to world health
- How antibiotics served up on factory farms can impact your own ability to fight off viruses and pathogens

Chapter 15:
- What some people are eating, and how that has led to disease
- Why bushmeat is a threat to your health, even if you don't eat it
- Common diseases passed from animals to humans, and how they get passed

Bonus Sections:
- The Antibiotic Conundrum
- Economics of a Plant-based Diet

Worksheets:
- Multiple Choice (or Not!)
- True – or Alternative Fact?
- Factory Farm Facts
- Self-Rating Scale
- Steps You Can Take
- Action Plan
- Other Points to Remember

The Antibiotic Conundrum

"Could I just have an antibiotic?" In recent decades, this request to doctors has been a common one for various ailments. Unfortunately, the accumulated side effects of the very frequent use of antibiotics are now coming "home to roost."

Whether you have taken an antibiotic in recent years or not, you have most likely been exposed to them in the foods you eat.[86] That's because agricultural antibiotic use (which accounts for about 70% of all antibiotic use in the U.S.), impacts humans as well.[87,88] In addition to coming through meat and dairy products, antibiotics filter into the food chain in other unexpected ways. For example, food crops (such as lettuce and potatoes) have been shown to accumulate antibiotics from manure used as fertilizer.[89] Even some organic food isn't totally safe, as organic farmers are allowed to use manure from factory farms (which use antibiotics freely).[90]

The Pandemic Within the Pandemic

Even more worrisome is the fact that the ineffectiveness of many tried-and-true antibiotics, or antimicrobial resistance as it is commonly called, has been made much worse by the COVID-19 pandemic. COVID-related factors that have increased antimicrobial resistance include:

- The excessive use of antimicrobial products like disinfectants, hand sanitizers, and other biocides.[91]
- The overuse of antibiotics to treat COVID-19 patients.[92]

It bears noting here that, since COVID-19 is caused by the SARS-CoV-2 virus, antibiotics are useless against it.[93] Despite this, antibiotics have been used liberally on COVID-19 patients with the hope that they could prevent bacterial co-infections. In a study of 38 Michigan hospitals, 56.6% of patients with COVID-19 were administered antibiotics early in their stay, even though only 3.5% of them ended up having a bacterial infection.[94] In other words, while the rate of bacterial co-infections was low, the use of antibiotics as a preventative measure remained high.

Because your mitochondria are targeted by certain antibiotics, therapy with these drugs can in fact weaken immune system response.[95] Antibiotics and disinfectants, while protecting against COVID-19, may also trigger allergies and/or inflammation.[96] As a result of these and other challenges, the CDC has declared antimicrobial resistance to be one of the top 10 public health threats to humans today.[97]

Antimicrobial resistance, which causes about 1.27 million deaths globally every year, is expected to reach as high as 10 million deaths per year by the year 2050.[98,99] The danger of antibiotic overuse was highlighted by a recent study stating that, in 2019, antimicrobial resistance took more lives than either HIV/AIDS (864,000 deaths) or malaria (643,000 deaths).[100]

The challenge of excess antibiotic intake resulting from those in the food chain plus unnecessary prescriptions, may, when combined with "preventative" prescriptions given to COVID-19 patients, render the immune system less capable of fighting off new infections.

What to Do?

Antibiotics serve as powerful agents against disease in many situations. However, in order to preserve their effectiveness when really needed, the instances in which antibiotics are used need to be carefully considered and, in most cases, drastically reduced.

A 3-step Plan

Following are some strategies to help you work in that direction:

- As much as possible, plan your diet around organic, antibiotic-free foods (including meat and animal products, if you eat them at all).
- Only use antibiotics for medical purposes when absolutely necessary. Generally speaking, a "necessity" would involve:

  o When a culture has been taken that reveals the exact infection
  o Other remedies are failing, and
  o An antibiotic has been shown to be specific against that specific infection.

- Avoid the overuse of household cleaners and disinfectants, which produce some of the same negative effects as the overuse of antibiotics.

Economics of a Plant-based Diet

From their childhood on, most people have known that eating vegetables (as well as fruits, nuts, and grains) is just flat-out healthy. While better health is certainly an important reason to focus on whole, plant-based foods, other good reasons are becoming increasingly more obvious as well. One of those reasons is money.

Easy on the Wallet

A new study conducted by the UK-based organization Veganuary (a charity dedicated to plant-based eating), which reviewed 11,000 weekly food diaries for a year, found that plant-based meals:

- Cost an average of 40% less than meals that include meat and dairy and
- Take one-third less time to prepare (when compared to meals involving meat and/or dairy products).[101]

When the old adage ("time is money") is considered, eating a plant-based diet results in a double monetary savings (time, which is equal to money), and money itself!

In another study, Veganuary researchers found that, when compared to their meat-eating counterparts, vegans saved an average of $23 on their grocery store bills each week. While plant-based products (such as meat substitutes and vegan dairy alternatives) can "up" the bill significantly, Veganuary's study found that plant-based meat alternatives only accounted for 3.7% of the yearly food and drink budget of study participants following a plant-based diet.[102] These findings fly in the face of the oft-repeated myth that eating a plant-based diet is more expensive than a diet that includes animal products.

More Savings to Be Had

For years now, researchers have been documenting that the more veggies, fruits, nuts and grains there are in the diet, the less your medical costs are likely to be. Some of the differences are truly astounding. Scientists from Loma Linda University's Adventist Health Studies (a long-term medical research project designed to measure the link between lifestyle, diet, disease and mortality of Seventh-day Adventists) have found that:

- Eating whole grains decreases the risk of a fatal heart attack by 45%
- Men who eat more tomatoes decrease their risk of prostate cancer by 40%, while men who drank soy milk reduce the risk of prostate cancer by 70%
- People who drink 5 or more glasses of water daily reduce heart attack risk by 50%
- A diet that includes legumes (such as beans and peas) reduces the risk of colorectal cancer. (In contrast, a diet that included red and white meat was associated with an increased risk of colorectal cancer).
- A diet rich in nuts decreased cardiovascular risk by 50%[103]

It goes without saying that the increase in health related to the above translates into millions and possibly billions of dollars in savings. In addition to lost productivity, the cost of treating disease related to meat-eating (as opposed to a plant-based diet) is truly significant.

The Polypharmacy Factor

A reduction in medications prescribed, and the associated cost, is another huge area of savings for those following a plant-based diet. The American Journal of Lifestyle Medicine reported that seniors following a full plant-based diet take 58% less medication than their meat-consuming counterparts.[104]

Researchers have reported that the average senior citizen (age 60 or older) takes five pharmaceutical prescriptions daily.[105] This practice has become so common that it even has a name: polypharmacy.

Polypharmacy is more common in older adults, many of whom suffer from multiple chronic conditions. For the elderly, adverse side effects of extra prescriptions may include cognitive impairment and/or increased risk of falling.[106] There is also the burden on either the elderly or their caregivers to understand the purpose of each medication, schedule dosages, manage refills, and watch for side effects.

The more prescriptions you take, the greater the risk of adverse side effects due to interactions between the medications.[107] These adverse side effects often lead to even more prescriptions, and thus the cycle continues.

A Staggering Cost

The economic cost of all the increased risk of disease and the pharmaceuticals used to treat it can hardly be estimated. One of the easiest ways to significantly reduce those staggering cost is quite simple: the plant-based whole foods diet which just happens to cost less at the grocery store checkout, as well.

Multiple Choice (or Not!)

After reviewing the chapter assignments, circle the correct answer(s) for each of the questions below. (Note – some questions have more than one right answer.)

1. The religious holidays of Lent, Yom Kippur, and Ramadan have the following in common:
 a. All are of Catholic origin
 b. All are of Jewish origin
 c. Each involves "giving something up" for a specified period of time
 d. Each celebrates Christmas in its own unique way

2. Scientists have discovered that a simple lifestyle change (such as "giving up" one thing) can:
 a. Provide a real boost to immune system function
 b. Be difficult if not impossible for children and the elderly
 c. Be the starting point of a downward spiral
 d. Only be done as part of a 12-step recovery plan

3. Sugar in the diet:
 a. Lowers immune system function virtually every time it is eaten
 b. Increases inflammatory markers in the bloodstream
 c. Leaches needed minerals from the body
 d. All of the above

4. White flour:
 a. Acts much the same way as sugar in the body
 b. Is extremely healthy, especially when enriched
 c. Is a primary ingredient in harmful, processed foods
 d. Is often combined with other harmful ingredients

5. Excessive salt intake contributes to:
 a. High blood pressure
 b. Poor immune system function
 c. Both of the above
 d. Neither of the above

6. Milk and milk-based products:
 a. Have been closely linked to cancer risk
 b. Contain morphine-like compounds which make them addictive
 c. Are linked to higher mucus production
 d. Create an inflammatory response

7. Fried foods in the diet:
 a. Increase inflammation
 b. Result in lower immune system function
 c. Are carcinogenic (e.g. have been identified as a causative factor in cancer)
 d. All of the above.

8. The consumption of processed and charred meats has been linked to:
 a. Longer, healthier lives
 b. Reduced immune system function
 c. Increased risk of colon cancer
 d. Systemic inflammation

9. Coffee has been found to:
 a. Trigger stress hormones, which in turn impairs immune system function
 b. Block the production of infection-fighting antibodies in the body
 c. Improve digestive function
 d. Contribute to insomnia

10. Consumption of alcohol can:
 a. Impair the body's immune system function for up to 24 hours
 b. Trigger fatty liver disease
 c. Contribute to higher blood pressure, body mass index, and cancer risk
 d. All the above

11. Chickens raised on factory farms are:
 a. Grown abnormally fast
 b. Penned in small spaces without fresh air, sunlight, or freedom to move
 c. Second only to pork in terms of positive health benefits
 d. Kept in a constant state of stress, which is very immunosuppressive

12. Public health experts worry about "Bird Flu" on chicken farms because it may:
 a. Endanger the water supply
 b. Negatively impact the quality of broiler chicken meat
 c. Jump to humans and cause a deadly pandemic
 d. Reduce overall egg production

True – or Alternative Fact?

Circle the correct True or False answer for each of the statements below:

1.	Because of the enlightened attitude of the American public, very few U.S. farm animals are raised on factory farms.	True	False
2.	Several viruses, including the Nipah Virus and H1N1 (Swine Flu), have already made the leap from pigs to humans.	True	False
3.	More than 80% of pigs have pneumonia at the time they are slaughtered.	True	False
4.	Dairy products often include elevated levels of pesticides, hormones, and antibiotics.	True	False
5.	Widespread overuse of antibiotics in factory farms is closely related to the antibiotic resistance gaining ground in the U.S. today.	True	False
6.	Nobody eats bushmeat anymore.	True	False
7.	One person eating a monkey can put the whole world at risk.	True	False
8.	The fact that 25,000 cases of leprosy are diagnosed in Brazil each year could be due to the high consumption of armadillos in that country.	True	False
9.	The HIV virus (AIDS) actually got its start from chimpanzee consumption.	True	False
10.	Anthrax, the Ebola Virus, and Rabies are three diseases that originated with animals and were passed to humans.	True	False

Factory Farm Facts

Meat and other animal products purchased from the supermarket, unless otherwise marked, are quite likely to be the products of factory farms. See if you can match the animals on the following list with the percentage that are raised on factory farms in the United States:

CHICKENS RAISED FOR MEAT	**98.3%**
CHICKENS RAISED FOR EGGS	**70.4%**
PIGS	**98.2%**
COWS	**99.8%**
TURKEYS	**99.9%**

Self-Rating Scale

INSTRUCTIONS: Circle the answer that fits you best.

	😃	😐	😟	😢
I have no problem giving things up if I learn they are bad for me:	That would be correct	Sometimes	That would be hard!	I don't think I can do it
Sugar is my favorite comfort food:	Not at all!	Very rarely	Quite often	Every day!
I love fried foods. If a food can be fried, I fry it!	No!	Only rarely	That's right!	Absolutely!
Dairy and/or animal products are a major part of my diet:	Not at all	Once in a while	Mostly, yes	Without fail!
I love donuts, white bread, pasta, and/or chips:	Not really	Once in a while	Pretty much	That's a given!
Coffee and/or alcohol are among my favorite drinks:	I don't drink them	Very rarely	Much of the time	Absolutely!
If I do consume animal products, they never make up more than 10% of my plate.	Always	Whenever I can	Sometimes	Never
I love eating exotic meat menu options:	Never	Rarely	Regularly	Every chance I get!
I eat a whole foods, plant-based diet:	Always	Most of the time	Rarely	What's a vegetable?

Review your answers in the previous section. Are there any simple and/or immediate steps you can take to improve in any of these areas? If so, list them below:

Steps I Can Take:

1 _____

_____

_____

2 _____

_____

_____

3 _____

_____

_____

4 _____

_____

_____

5 _____

_____

_____

Action Plan

Review the "Action Plan" from chapters 8, 14, and 15 as summarized below. Put a check mark by the ones you are ready to work on:

- ○ Review the "Diet No-go's" for pandemic times of sugar, white flour (and processed foods in general), excess salt, milk (and other dairy products), fried foods, meat, alcohol, and coffee. Write down which ones you would like to "give up" in order to boost your immune system.

- ○ Consider your current diet. If you are eating forms of meat that may increase your risk of disease, look for and try out some "eat this not that" alternatives that might appeal to you.

- ○ If you think curtailing chicken, dairy, or other animal product consumption would be too hard, watch some documentaries on factory farming. For anyone who loves animals, these can be highly motivational in terms of positive change.

- ○ If you are consuming foods that might include antibiotics, consider what alternatives you might try.

- ○ If you have a taste for "wild," unusual or exotic meat, or are:
  - Using traditional remedies that contain unusual ingredients drawn from some animal part, or
  - Handling or otherwise coming in contact with these types of meats in your line of work,
  - Consider how you can reduce your risk of contracting a zoonotic disease through contact with animals, then make and implement a plan.

Other Points to Remember

Are there other points you would like to remember from the chapters covered in this session? If so, write them here:

_____

_____

_____

_____

_____

_____

_____

Chapter Assignments:
Chapter 11: Eat, Drink & Be Strong

What You'll Learn:
At the end of this session, you will have a better understanding of:

Chapter 11:
- The strong connection between insulin resistance and immune system function
- The powerful role of nitric oxide in fighting health threats, and how to get more of this vital nutrient
- One of the easiest ways to remember the best foods to eat (G-BOMBS®)
- The lowdown on each one of the G-BOMBS® and why you should eat them

Bonus Sections:
- Is a 100% Raw Diet the Healthiest Choice?
- Why the Phytochemicals in Your Diet Should Come from Food (Not Supplements)

Worksheets:
- Multiple Choice (or Not!)
- True – or Alternative Fact?
- G-BOMB® Quiz
- Self-Rating Scale
- Steps You Can Take
- Action Plan
- Other Points to Remember

Is a 100% Raw Diet the Healthiest Choice?

Most people know that raw fruit, vegetables, and even nuts are healthy foods. The live enzymes in raw plant-based foods, and their healing properties, are simply good for overall health. Raw foodists take things one step further by maintaining that a 100% raw food diet is the very best option for health. Others disagree. Who is right? Who is wrong? Or is the truth somewhere in the middle? We'll take a look at pros and cons, and answer some important questions, below.

Benefits of a Raw Food Diet

As a therapeutic diet, many have found raw fruits and veggies to be not only packed with nutrients, but easier to digest. Raw foodists point out, correctly, that some valuable enzymes, antioxidants, and vitamins are destroyed in the cooking process.[108]

Raw foods tend to alkalize the body, resulting in less acidity, which translates into less inflammation.[109] When the body is more acidic, the immune system is hampered, raising the risk of disease.[110] Although non-food factors (such as environmental pollution, mineral deficient water, and stress) can contribute to acidosis in the body, they are not the only culprit.[111] Processed foods, poor nutrition, and a diet too high in even healthy cooked foods can contribute to a dangerous, less alkaline state.[112]

Cooked foods (especially highly processed ones) tend to sit in the digestive tract longer, raising the risk of fermentation and other challenges in the gut.[113] When food ferments in the gut, proteins putrefy and fats go rancid. Toxic waste accumulates and inflammation sets in, which will eventually damage the mucosal lining of the gut. This leads to leaky gut syndrome (where toxins from the body's "sewer system" seeps into the body's vital organs, wreaking havoc wherever they go). Eating a diet with a higher percentage of raw plant-based foods is one of the best ways to keep things moving in the intestines and avoid toxic buildup in the body.[114]

In addition, researchers have found that a raw food plant-based diet can result in:
- Better digestion and regularity[115]
- Improved function of the heart, liver, and kidneys[116]
- Reduced risk of arthritis, autoimmune disorders, cancer, food allergies, headaches, osteoporosis, muscle aches and pains, and Parkinson's[117]
- Less PMS and better hormonal balance overall[118]
- More energy[119]
- Clearer skin[120]
- Healthier body weight[121]

Benefits of Cooked Food

"Cooking kills the enzymes in the food" is a major argument put forth by raw food proponents. It is true that cooking degrades the nutrients in some foods. However, the act of cooking heps release the nutrients in other foods, while making still others more digestible.[122]

In the case of foods that are rich in beta-carotene and lycopene (such as squash, sweet potatoes, and tomatoes), cooking is especially beneficial. In such produce, heat helps release the nutrients, making them more bioavailable to the body.[123] This in addition to making many of them taste much better! Other veggies that benefit from cooking include:

- Cruciferous vegetables (such as broccoli, cabbage, cauliflower, and kale). The goitrogen compounds in these foods, when eaten raw and in excess, can block thyroid function or even trigger hyperthyroidism. These potentially problematic compounds are deactivated by cooking, however.[124]
- Peppers and mushrooms, which some researchers have found to be more nutrient-dense when cooked.[125]
- Legumes can be enjoyed much more easily when cooked. (Legumes eaten on a raw foods diet must be sprouted.)[126]

Conclusion

Most people would do well to eat a lot more fruits and vegetables daily, with some cooked and some raw. Current dietary guidelines for Americans recommend 2 cups of fruit and 2 ½ cups of vegetables.[127] Most Americans eat far less than that, with the average being half a cup of fruit and 1 ½ cups of veggies daily.[128]

Eating more vegetables—especially "in the raw"—can be particularly beneficial for the more than 65% of Americans who are overweight or obese. The food density of raw vegetables makes it possible to eat a lot more, and feel much more satisfied, than with other foods.

While a raw plant-based diet does have its therapeutic advantages, it bears noting that no human civilization has ever survived long-term on a raw foods diet. The healthiest, most sustainable diet would be a whole foods, plant-based diet that includes a balance of raw and cooked foods.

Why the Phytochemicals in Your Diet Should Come from Food (Not Supplements)

There's been quite a buzz about phytochemicals in recent years, and with good reason. These natural chemicals, which are found in foods, play an important role in helping the body to function properly.[129] Phytochemicals also help protect against chronic diseases such as heart disease, and cancer.[130]

What are Phytochemicals?

The word phyto comes from the Greek word meaning plant. Sometimes referred to as phytonutrients, these chemical compounds are the ones that give plants their various colors, aromas, and flavors.[131]

Phytochemicals help determine a plant's color. These colors (red, blue, yellow, green, orange, purple, and white) help us to identify the type of phytochemicals contained in a plant. For example, the orange of beta-carotene is associated with vegetables of that color (such as carrots). Some of the most well-known phytochemicals, together with their vegetable sources, include:

- Flavanoids - fruit (apples and cranberries), coffee, and tea
- Curcuminoids - turmeric and mustard
- Lycopene - tomatoes, red peppers, and watermelon
- Isoflavonoids - soybeans, peanuts, and chickpeas
- Carotenoids - carrots (beta-carotene) and dark, leafy greens
- Polyphenols - grapes (and wine), berries (black, blue, and raspberries)
- Allyl Sulfides - garlic, chives, and leeks
- Phenolic acids - herbs and legumes[132]

Health Benefits of Phytochemicals

Although they aren't considered essential nutrients like Vitamin C, phytochemical compounds are invaluable to your health. They can boost your immune system, support detoxification, reduce inflammation and regulate hormones.[133] They also help plants resist fungi and bacterial or viral infections.[134]

Studies show that some phytochemicals are anti-inflammatory.[135] Other phytochemicals, such as those found in broccoli, kale, Brussel sprouts, and cauliflower, may:

- Suppress tumor growth
- Limit cancer-related hormone production and
- Counteract cancer-causing agents in your body.[136]

Supplement Companies to the Rescue (Or Not!)

Recognizing the many health benefits of phytochemicals, many supplement companies have tried to make it so that people could get their "daily dose" of these valuable nutrients by simply taking a pill. The problem with this approach is that researchers have identified more than 3,000 types of phytonutrients.[137] While a few types of phytochemicals might be packed into a pill, there's only one way to get the full range of nutrition nature offers: eat the rainbow! Since the different colors of food represent different phytochemicals, you are getting a lot of nutrition when you put a variety of plant-based, colorful foods on your plate.

Other Supplement Challenges

Other challenges with supplements identified by researchers include that they:

- Don't provide the best combination of nutrients and phytochemicals to sustain the body[138]
- May not be as easily absorbed by the body as those from whole foods,[139] and/or
- Can be toxic, or even cause cancer, in higher doses.[140]

Isn't the Soil Depleted?

Some people prefer to take supplements because they worry about the nutritional depletion of the earth's soil today as opposed to decades ago. This may be true to a certain degree, but if the soil was not rich in nutrients, would plants still be growing?

The Bible tells us that the earth will always provide the food needed to nourish us. In other words, there will always be life-sustaining food to eat until the end of time. "For as long as Earth lasts, planting and harvest, cold and heat, summer and winter, day and night will never stop." (Genesis 8:22, The Message Bible)

If you are worried about the nutritional deficiencies in soil or pesticides, try growing your own vegetables and buying organic produce that's pesticide free. Alternatively, always wash all non-organic fruit and vegetables thoroughly to reduce exposure to pesticides.

Multiple Choice (or Not!)

After reviewing the chapter assignments, circle the correct answer(s) for each of the questions below. (Note – some questions have more than one right answer.)

1. Nitric oxide, which is known as the "miracle molecule":
a. Is harder for human bodies to produce after the age of 70
b. Is easily obtained by eating bacon, hot dogs, and ham
c. Is a vital first line of defense against viral infections
d. Is a powerful blood circulation optimizer

2. Foods rich in natural nitrates include:
a. Nuts and seeds
b. Leafy greens
c. Garlic
d. Honey Baked Ham

3. Insulin resistance:
a. Is a huge problem in the U.S., where it affects 60-70 million individuals
b. Impacts the immune system in very significant ways
c. Has no relationship to fat in the diet
d. Responds best to a whole foods, plant-based diet

4. Healthy foods recommended in the G-BOMB® acronym include:
a. Greens, berries and beans
b. Onions, garlic, and mushrooms
c. Nuts and seeds
d. Oreo® cookies

5. Greens:
a. Are some of the healthiest foods on the planet
b. Strengthen the immune system
c. Are rich in chlorophyll
d. Help to remove harmful toxins and impurities from the blood

6. Beans:
a. Cause lots of gas, so shouldn't be eaten
b. Are high in health-promoting antioxidants
c. Provide an excellent source of fiber, folate, and protein
d. Are beneficial to good gut bacteria

7. Onions, garlic, and their allium cousins:
a. Cause bad breath, so shouldn't be eaten (especially at social occasions)
b. Are very beneficial to the immune system and overall health
c. Are rich in vitamins, minerals, and other health-promoting compounds
d. Have an anti-inflammatory effect on the body

8. Mushrooms have been shown to:
a. Help with weight management
b. Eradicate viruses, bacteria, and yeast
c. Overrun the body with harmful fungus-like substances
d. Boost the immune system

9. Seeds:
a. Are extremely nutritious because they contain all the nutrients to develop an entire plant
b. Are loaded with unhealthy fats
c. Should never be eaten raw
d. Are packed with vitamins, minerals, and antioxidants

10. Almonds and walnuts:
a. Are the "superstars" in the nut category of food
b. Are unhealthy and should not be eaten
c. Contain the vitamin E needed by the immune system to ward off invading bacteria
d. Are a source of healthy fats

11. Berries are:
a . Best left for bears to eat
b. One of nature's best sources of antioxidants in the diet
c. Low in calories
d. Rich in compounds that boost the immune response

12 The three powerful, health-promoting antioxidants found in berries include:
a. Anthocyanins
b. Anthocyanide
c. Quercetin
d. Vitamin C

True – or Alternative Fact?

Circle the correct True or False answer for each of the statements below:

1.	Nitric oxide in the diet helps with vasodilation, a process which relaxes and widens the inner blood vessels, resulting in increased circulation and lower blood pressure.	**True**	**False**
2.	Added nitrates in the diet from foods such as bacon, deli meat, hot dogs, and ham, have been strongly linked to cancer, among other health challenges.	**True**	**False**
3.	The G-BOMBS® acronym, which serves as a powerful reminder of the best foods to eat, was devised by Benjamin Franklin.	**True**	**False**
4.	Spinach has been shown to improve red blood cell function, strengthen bones, regulate blood pressure and heart rate, and combat free radicals.	**True**	**False**
5.	The protein in beans has virtually no impact on the body's ability to build immune system cells.	**True**	**False**
6.	Beans have been shown to be protective against cancer (due to their antioxidant and anti-inflammatory properties).	**True**	**False**
7.	Chives, garlic, onions, and leeks all contain flavonoids which promote the production of glutathione, a powerful antioxidant which has been shown to boost the immune system and help detox the body.	**True**	**False**
8.	Eating garlic and onions is particularly bad for cardiovascular health.	**True**	**False**
9.	Researchers have found that people who eat nuts on a regular basis live longer and healthier lives.	**True**	**False**
10.	Flax seeds are high in helpful omega-3 fats.	**True**	**False**

G-BOMB® Quiz

One of the best ways to remember the healthiest foods to eat is by using the G-BOMBS® acronym coined by Dr. Joel Furhman. Draw lines to match the appropriate G-BOMBS® food group with some of its benefits below:

Greens	This food represents the entire Allium family, which is rich in antioxidants, flavonoids, and other healing properties.
Beans	This food boosts the immune system, destroys cancer cells, fights against viruses, and can even help with weight management!
Onions	These tiny foods are one of nature's best sources of antioxidants, including anthocyanins, quercetin, and vitamin C.
Mushrooms	Some of the healthiest foods on the planet, these plant foods promote oxygenation and blood flow. (Hint: they get their vibrant color from chlorophyll).
Berries	These heart-healthy superstar foods are packed with some of the most nutrition on the planet.
Seeds	Rich in fiber and folate, these nutritional powerhouses are particularly healthful for the heart and gut.

Self-Rating Scale

INSTRUCTIONS: Circle the answer that fits you best.

	😊	😟	🙁	😢
If I'm late for a meal, my blood sugar starts to go low:	Not at all	Maybe a little	Quite a bit	I can't miss a meal!
I eat plenty of fruits and veggies, both raw and cooked, every day:	Of course!	Most of the time	Some of the time	Do French fries count?
I love salads! And cooked green vegetables, too:	Definitely yes!	For the most part	Not so much	I never eat anything green
Onions and garlic are a frequent part of my diet:	Always	Frequently	Sometimes	Never
I eat berries on a regular basis:	All the time	Quite a bit	Once in a while	Hardly ever
Raw seeds and / or nuts are a frequent part of my menu:	Always	Most of the time	Sometimes	Not at all
My diet is a healthy balance of raw and cooked plant-based whole foods:	Every day!	Most of the time	Sometimes	Not!
I eat beans at least once a day:	Always	Most of the time	Sometimes	They don't agree with me!
Several types of mushrooms are included in my diet:	Yes	Maybe one type	Once in a while	I hate mushrooms!

Review your answers in the previous section. Are there any simple and/or immediate steps you can take to improve in any of these areas? If so, list them below:

Steps I Can Take:

1 _____

_____

_____

_____

2 _____

_____

_____

_____

_____

3 _____

_____

_____

_____

4 _____

_____

_____

_____

5 _____

_____

_____

_____

Action Plan

**Review the "Action Plan" from chapter 11 as summarized below.
Put a check mark by the ones you are ready to work on:**

○   I am getting enough nitric oxide in my diet from natural sources.

○   The foods I eat keep my blood sugar levels stable.

○   I eat all of the G-BOMB® food categories on a regular basis.

○   There are still some ways that I can improve my diet (Please list them below under "Other Points to Remember.")

Other Points to Remember

Are there other points you would like to remember from the chapters covered in this session? If so, write them here:

_____

_____

_____

_____

_____

_____

_____

_____

_____

_____

_____

_____

Chapter Assignments:
Chapter 9: Dress to Suppress
Chapter 12: Let the Sun Shine In

What You'll Learn:
At the end of this session, you will have a better understanding of:

Chapter 9:
- The 5 clothing choices that can actually make you sick
- Why maintaining the right core body temperature promotes immune system health
- How tight clothing limits circulation – and health
- Toxic fabrics that can actually harm your health, plus the very best fabrics to wear

Chapter 12:
- 6 ways sunshine boosts the immune system
- The healing impact of different colors of light
- Blue light and its powerful impact – morning and evening
- How sunshine and exercise are alike
- The vitamin D connection to sunshine, immune system function, and COVID-19

Bonus Sections:
- The Magic of Morning Sunshine
- For Success, Do Not Overdress!

Worksheets:
- Multiple Choice (or Not!)
- True – or Alternative Fact?
- "Good" Fabric Facts
- Self-Rating Scale
- Steps You Can Take
- Action Plan
- Other Points to Remember

The Magic of Morning Sunshine

When you expose your skin to a healthy dose of sunshine, good things are sure to follow. Researchers have reported that the warm, soothing rays of the sun can:

- Increase energy[141]
- Support better sleep[142]
- Lower the risk of metabolic syndrome[143]
- Heal inflammation[144], and
- Reduce cancer risk[145].

Most people know that sunlight is also a major source of vitamin D, which has been shown to protect against inflammation, improve brain function, and lower blood pressure.[146] What might not be as well-known is the impact of sunshine on mood-boosting hormones (such as serotonin and dopamine).

Sunlight and the "Happy Hormones"

Researchers have found that sunlight increases the release of serotonin (one of the body's mood-boosting, feel-good hormones) to the brain.[147] In addition to increasing our happiness quotients, serotonin helps us feel calmer and more focused.[148] Serotonin also triggers the release of melatonin — another important mood-related hormone[149].

Melatonin helps to regulate the body's sleep-wake cycle, known as the circadian rhythm.[150] With enough melatonin, we are likely to sleep better at night—and nothing increases dopamine levels like a good night of rest.[151] (Dopamine the feel-good, happy hormone associated with rewards, euphoria, and pure bliss![152]) Needless to say, the release of extra dopamine is also very beneficial to one's general mood and outlook on life!

Together, these "Happy Hormones" of the body play a huge role in regulating our energy levels and stabilizing our emotions.

Morning Sunshine to the Rescue

Researchers who studied the impact of sunlight on health and moods have discovered a very interesting fact: not all sunlight is created equal. Exposure to morning sunlight (usually at around 6 a.m.) results in greater serotonin production than sunlight exposure at other times of the day.[153]

The increased levels of serotonin triggered by exposure to early morning sun have been found to protect against both depression, disrupted sleep patterns, and/or insomnia.[154] The resulting lack of sleep, in turn:

- Weakens the immune system[155]
- Takes a toll on mental and physical health[156]
- Leads to daytime tiredness, lethargy, irritability, and depression.[157]

Small Doses Suffice

It doesn't take a large dose of sunlight to give the body what it requires. 10-20 minutes of exposure to early morning light is all that is needed.[158] Too much sunlight exposure can actually result in headaches, due to an overload of serotonin being sent to the brain.[159] Excess sunlight exposure (more than 40 minutes) to the strong midday rays of the sun can also damage the skin.[160] If you are at the beach soaking up sunshine midday, be sure to apply at least SPF 30 sunscreen.

"Workarounds" for People Who Need Them

Unfortunately, many people are not in a situation where they can go "catch a few rays" at 6 a.m. in the morning. They may live in Alaska (where the sun shines irregularly), be racing off to work, or already be working in a building where there are no windows. Thankfully, there is a workaround for people who don't have the opportunity to get regular morning sun: blue light therapy.

Blue Light Therapy—An Answer

For those who work long hours indoors or don't have access to the early morning sun, modern technology has provided a ready solution. Blue light therapy can be used to replicate the intake of morning sunlight.[161] To be most effective, any therapeutic light purchased should be a medical grade blue light with at least 10,000 lux.[162] Though nothing can beat the natural rays of the sun, blue light therapy has been shown to:

- Improve mood in those suffering from depression[163]
- Be effective as a treatment against insomnia[164], and
- Protect against Seasonal Affective Disorder (SAD)

Many people struggling with these maladies have found the purchase of a blue light to be a very wise investment in their health. (Note: Never look at a blue light directly, as that can damage the retina.)[166]

When considering how to boost your immune system, overall health, and mood, don't forget the importance of morning sunlight. A good dose of light—whether from natural sunshine or in the form of light therapy—will help to regulate the natural rhythms of both your body and mind.

With the stress of living in our modern-day world, there is no better time to use the light of the sun to increase our "Happiness Hormones."

For Success, Do Not Overdress!

"Dress for success" is a time-honored adage that has been repeated often over the years. Another important principle that isn't much thought of, however, can have a significant impact on your health: "For success, do not overdress!"

While wearing enough clothing is certainly important, wearing too much (or the wrong things) can be positively harmful. The bad habit of overdressing started in the 18th and 19th century. During those "fashionable" days, wealthy people wore so many clothing items and accessories that it could literally take an hour just to get dressed every day![167]

Of Fops and Fools

One example of 18th century overdressing was the "fop"—a word meaning a "fool" that was applied to men who put on "graces and airs." Fops were especially known for their attention to the latest whims of fashion and their outrageously elaborate clothing ensembles. Tight breeches, fancy waistcoats with lace trim and elaborate buttons, skirted lace-trimmed satin or velvet coats, neckcloths, elaborate wigs, and high-heeled shoes were all worn by men back in the day.[168]

Not to be outdone, wealthy women of the past often wore luxurious gowns with exaggerated bustles and long trains. Hoops, corsets, lace neck frills, sleeve ruffles, and wired headdresses were also popular accessories.

While many of the fashion trends of centuries gone by seem extravagant or silly now, some were positively harmful to health. Tightly fastened corsets, long skirts dragging in the mud, unwieldy hoop skirts, and even high heels all took their toll.[169]

Challenges of Today

While the fashion trends of today are much different than those of centuries past, some are a real challenge to the health of the body. Following is a short list of some of the most dangerous fashions:

High Heels

Health challenges created by wearing high heels include:
- Increased risk of ankle sprain. (High heels are one of the main reasons why women sprain their ankles.)[170]
- Irritation to the toes (which in some cases requires surgery to correct).[171]
- An unhealthy alignment of the hips which may cause pain, an abnormal curvature of the spine, or chronic back trouble.[172]
- Damage to muscles and tendons.[173]

For female footwear, shorter pumps would be a much better choice than stilettos, with elegant flats being the best choice of all.

Girdles

Girdles or other "waist training" apparatuses do more than restrict movement. They may also decrease lung capacity and ultimately, overall strength.[174]

Toxic Makeup

Researchers at the University of California–Berkeley found large amounts of toxins (such as cadmium, chromium, and lead) in 75% of lipstick samples tested.[175] If you wear a toxic lipstick, toxins seep into your pores virtually every time you apply it!

Common toxins found in lipstick include:
- Aluminum—which researchers have found may cause Alzheimer's, anemia, and osteoporosis—among other diseases.[176]
- Cadmium—a documented cancer-causing agent that has been found in many breast cancer biopsies.[177]
- Chromium—which has been connected to stomach cancer.[178]
- Lead—which can result in decreased IQ, irreversible brain cell damage, and personality disorders.[179]

If you wear lipstick and want to learn more, refer to the FDA's list of the worst lipstick toxins,[180] then check the ingredients on the makeup you are using.

Heavy Purses

Hauling around a heavy bag can lead to aches and pains in the head, neck, and shoulder areas.[181]

Restrictive Clothing

Though already mentioned in the book, tight clothing is so harmful that it bears mentioning again. Any clothing that restricts blood flow is bad for your health. In men, skinny jeans can lead to infertility and/or a painful condition called testicular torsion (where lack of circulation leads to loss of the testicle).[182] Tight pants can also lead to numbness and/or permanent nerve damage.[183] There is even a "tight pants syndrome," which is characterized by abdominal discomfort, belching, heartburn, and/or other digestive challenges.[184]

Bottom line: Unless you have been prescribed compression stockings for some medical reason, tight clothing should be avoided!

Multiple Choice (or Not!)

After reviewing the chapter assignments, circle the correct answer(s) for each of the questions below. (Note – some questions have more than one right answer.)

1. Getting chilled can:
a. Weaken the immune system and the body's power to fight infections
b. Happen when the feet aren't kept warm
c. Make it easier to catch a "bug"
d. None of the above

2. A protective, blood-flow reducing mechanism the body uses when faced with cold is known as the:
a. Reflex Effect
b. Contraction of Pneumonia
c. Great Immune System Mobilizer
d. Reflux Effect

3. Wearing tight clothes can:
a. Increase blood flow to certain areas of the body
b. Inhibit blood flow
c. Result in pain, acid reflux, and/or digestive issues
d. Reduce the ability of the immune system to perform at an optimal level

4. Dressing too warmly in hot weather:
a. Is totally unrelated to health
b. Can decrease immune system function
c. Puts a strain on the body's cooling system
d. Is very important, especially in Peru

5. Continuing to wear pants or leggings after a sweaty workout:
a. Increases the risk of skin, bacterial, and yeast infections
b. Helps the body to avoid dehydration
c. Should not be done
d. Is safest if the clothing is made from nonbreathable fabric

6. Researchers have found that the wearing of tight clothing:
a. Decreases bowel movement size
b. Reduces autonomic nervous system function
c. Lowers musculature activity of the trunk
d. All of the above

7. Toxic fabrics that may harm your health include:
a. Polyester
b. Rayon and Nylon
c. Bamboo and cotton-based fabrics
d. Spandex

8. Diarrhea-causing viruses:
a. Can last for a few weeks in the laundry
b. Can grow and thrive in unwashed laundry
c. Last longer than coronaviruses in the laundry
d. Can be eradicated through a normal wash cycle

9. The best clothes to wear would be:
a. Loose-fitting enough to allow good circulation
b. Free of toxic chemicals
c. Of breathable fabric and regularly washed
d. All of the above

10. The healthiest fabrics to wear include:
a. Cashmere, cotton, and hemp
b. Linen and/or silk
c. Polyester blends
d. Merino wool

11. Sunlight:
a. Provides the body with vitamin D
b. Serves as a disinfectant
c. Energizes the body's infection-fighting T cells
d. Aids in the body's absorption of immune-boosting minerals such as calcium and phosphorous

12 Benefits of red light therapy include:
a. Nitric oxide production
b. Lymphatic stimulation
c. Faster wound healing
d. All of the above

True – or Alternative Fact?

Circle the correct True or False answer for each of the statements below:

1.	Perfect health requires perfect circulation.	**True**	**False**
2.	The wearing of tight clothing is unrelated to back pain.	**True**	**False**
3.	Blood, feces, and saliva-borne pathogens can all be transmitted by dirty laundry.	**True**	**False**
4.	Researchers have found polyester to have anti-aging, anti-asthma, anti-eczema, and anti-fungal properties.	**True**	**False**
5.	Time in a tanning booth is the best way to benefit from soaking in the entire spectrum of healing light.	**True**	**False**
6.	Although ultraviolet light is beneficial, too much can contribute to the formation of skin cancer.	**True**	**False**
7.	Exposure to blue light at night can help you to get to sleep.	**True**	**False**
8.	85% of people with severe COVID-19 were found to have vitamin D deficiency.	**True**	**False**
9.	COVID-19 sufferers with vitamin D deficiency had 4-5 times the mortality rate of people with normal vitamin D levels.	**True**	**False**
10.	Vitamin D supplementation contributes to obesity.	**True**	**False**

"Good" Fabric Facts

Some of the best fabrics to wear, as featured in Chapter 9, are listed below.
Draw lines to match the "good" fabrics with some of their benefits:

Bamboo	With its smooth and silky feel, this natural fabric feels amazing against the skin as well.
Cashmere	Known for its strength and durability, this popular clothing fabric holds its shape well, and softens with use.
Cotton	This breathable, comfortable, hypoallergenic and durable material is easy to care for and suitable for every season.
Hemp	A fascinating new option, this biodegradable fabric is breathable, hypoallergenic, thermo-regulating, silky, and soft.
Linen	This lightweight, soft fabric is an all-natural, temperature and moisture regulating option that offers UV protection and doesn't sag or lose shape over time.
Merino Wool	Renowned for its luxurious texture, this fabric packs a powerful health benefit punch and can even improve sleep.
Silk	This comfortable, time-honored fabric is breathable, durable, hypoallergenic, absorbs sweat well, and works with the body to protect against temperature changes.

Self-Rating Scale

INSTRUCTIONS: Circle the answer that fits you best.

	😊	😐	🙁	😢
My jeans are so tight, I have to lay down to zip them up:	Not a chance!	Not usually	Most of the time	That's all I wear!
I never worry about getting chilled, and it does happen a lot:	No, I dress warmly	I rarely get chilled	Frequently	I get cold a lot!
I wash my clothes, sheets, and towels on a regular basis:	Like clockwork!	Most of the time	I'm a bit haphazard about it	I rarely ever do laundry
My wardrobe consists mostly of synthetic fabrics:	Not at all	Some of it	Most of it	That's all I wear!
I get at least half an hour of sunshine every day:	Absolutely!	Most of the time	Sometimes	Rarely
I either get some first morning light, or use blue light therapy:	Always	Most of the time	Sometimes	Not at all
I avoid blue light at night for at least an hour before going to bed:	That's my habit!	Not as much as I should	Sometimes	Not!
My vitamin D level has been tested and is where it ought to be:	Yes	Yes, more than a year ago	A long time ago	Never!
I take vitamin D supplements if my level gets low or I've had challenges in that area.	Yes	Most of the time	Sporadically	Never

Review your answers in the previous section. Are there any simple and/or immediate steps you can take to improve in any of these areas? If so, list them below:

Steps I Can Take:

1 _____
_____
_____
_____

2 _____
_____
_____
_____

3 _____
_____
_____
_____

4 _____
_____
_____
_____

5 _____
_____
_____
_____

Action Plan

Review the "Action Plan" from chapters 9 and 12 as summarized below.
Put a check mark by the ones you are ready to work on:

○ Are you often chilled, or often overheated and sweating? If so, consider what you can do to relieve your body of cold or heat stress.

○ Consider the fabrics you are wearing. If you are already prone to eczemas or allergies, take a look at your wardrobe with an eye for how you could reduce the toxins faced by your body's largest organ.

○ Consider whether you are getting enough sunlight in your life. If not, make a plan to get out and catch some rays!

○ Think about your nighttime routine. Are you using blue screen technology until just before going to bed? If so, consider the health consequences and what you could do to improve.

○ If you've never had your vitamin D checked, or haven't had it checked lately, consider that now might be a good time. If you find that you aren't able to get enough vitamin D either through sunlight exposure or diet, you might want to check into supplementation.

Other Points to Remember

Are there other points you would like to remember from the chapters covered in this session? If so, write them here:

_____

_____

_____

_____

_____

_____

_____

Chapter Assignments:
Chapter 13: Move More, Sit Less

What You'll Learn:
At the end of this session, you will have a better understanding of:

Chapter 13:
- Why sitting too much is an independent risk factor for a weak immune system
- What happens to your body when you sit for 1, 2, 4, or 6 hours
- The obesity-COVID-19 connection
- Why you should not only stand more, but squat!
- Why being more active is one of the fastest ways to improve your health
- The powerful impact of exercise on immune system function and overall health
- Why exercise as a remedy is so much more powerful than drugs
- Walking – and why it is one of the very best forms of exercise
- How to get started walking, even if you have sore knees
- A 10-step interval training program for walkers

Bonus Sections:
- Is High Intensity Interval Training (HIIT) the "Magic Bullet" for Fat Loss?
- "Sitting" Ourselves Up for Trouble

Worksheets:
- Multiple Choice (or Not!)
- True – or Alternative Fact?
- Sitting on Statistics
- Self-Rating Scale
- Steps You Can Take
- Action Plan
- Other Points to Remember

Is High Intensity Interval Training the "Magic Bullet" for Fat Loss?

I n recent years, High Intensity Interval Training (HIIT) has been recommended by many fitness experts as the missing ingredient for successful weight loss. HIIT is a form of interval training that involves:

- Short periods of intense (but not all-out) exercise or "sprints"
- A less active recovery period following each sprint

On a scale of 1-10, the "sprints" would be performed at an intensity of 6-8. In contrast, the active recovery period would be at an intensity level of 1-3. Many exercisers combine HIIT with cardio, weights or other forms of exercise. HIIT workouts, which normally take 30-40 minutes each, are usually performed 3-4 times per week.

Why is HIIT So Popular?
Researchers have found HIIT routines outdo continuous cardio by:

- Producing the same benefits in less time[185]
- Burning more fat overall[186], and
- Revving up the body's metabolism for hours after the exercise is performed[187].

Despite the highly publicized advantages of HIIT, continuous cardio exercises (such as taking a walk or peddling on a bike) is still the best option for individuals who:

- Lack the physical stamina to engage in HIIT, or
- Can't stick with a HIIT routine.

Most people who exercise regularly using a HIIT routine still engage in continuous cardio. In recent years, a sub-category of HIIT, known as Sprint Interval Training (SIT), has become quite popular. SIT sprints involve 100% all-out exertion every time. Because of the higher intensity, SIT sprints and workouts are shorter than those in HIIT. For example, a SIT workout might include:

- 4-6 thirty-second sprints at an intensity of 10
- A complete rest of 2-4 minutes between each sprint

Scientists Measure the Methods
Recently, a group of researchers analyzed more than 70 scientific studies related to continuous cardio, HIIT, and SIT. Their goal was to document which protocol was most efficient at reducing body fat percentage.

During the 9 weeks analyzed, the average exercise time for participants was:

- 2 ¼ hours per week for continuous cardio, which the researchers called Moderate Intensity Cardio Training, or MICT
- 1 hour and 42 minutes for HIIT, and
- 40 minutes for SIT.

The researchers also noted that SIT participants:

- Engaged in 16% fewer workouts each week than their MICT counterparts, and
- Spent 81% less time sprinting than HIIT exercisers.

Despite these factors, the scientists found that SIT resulted in a:

- 40% higher reduction in body fat percentage than HIIT, and a
- 92% higher reduction in body fat percentage than MICT.

In terms of overall body fat reduction over the course of the study:

- MICT participants lost 1.2% body fat
- HIIT participants lost 1.7% body fat
- SIT participants lost 2.3% body fat

The researchers concluded that HIIT is superior to MICT in terms of burning body fat.[188] In addition, SIT is superior to both MICT and HIIT. These results were especially impressive in light of the fact that SIT workouts required only a third of the time to perform as HIIT workouts, and even less when compared to MICT.

The differences in time spent sprinting during the study was also profound. HIIT participants sprinted for more than seven hours while SIT participants sprinted for just over one, while MICT participants (who spent a lot more time exercising) never sprinted at all.

What Makes SIT So Effective?
How did SIT outperform other forms of cardio training—in terms of body fat percentage reduction—in about half the time? The answer is found in the fact that SIT routines push the body out of homeostasis, which is its "comfort zone." The more intense the workout, the farther the body is pushed out of homeostasis, kickstarting the biological processes that resulted in greater and faster reductions in body fat. This is how SIT burned 40% more fat than HIIT in 60% less time.

Bottom Line: If you want quicker results and are physically able to do HIIT or SIT, you might want to give them a try—especially if finding time to exercise is a real challenge in your life.

"Sitting" Ourselves Up for Trouble

Most people sit too much. As shown in the illustration on this page, many also sit in an unhealthy way. Both of these practices are bad for circulation, bad for the immune system, and bad for overall health.[189] Whether you are a sedentary worker or simply feel you are sitting too much, the information on this page is meant to motivate you to, if needed, move more and sit less!

The Biomechanics of Sitting

THE IDEAL POSTURE

If you use a laptop instead of a desktop computer in your home office, your "set-up" will need to be modified to promote the best angle of vision, distance, and posture. Here are some recommendations:

These measurements are for a person about 5.5 feet (1.7 meters) tall.

- The notebook should have a slight tilt below where the eye is focused.
- To achieve this you might use a laptop holder or even a pair of books.

10° - 25°

27.5 in (70 cm)

Forearm Support

External Keyboard Helps to achieve better positioning for the arm[190]

Keeping the screen brightness low and softening the contrast is better for your eyes.[191]

Desk Height 21 in 74 cm

Lumbar Support 27.5 in 70 cm

Seat Height 18.5 in 74 cm

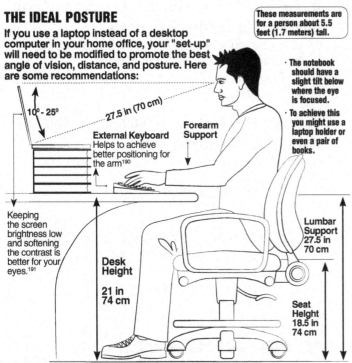

Sitting Opportunities for the Sedentary Worker During the Day

45 minutes	→	Drive to work
4 hours	→	Work on computer
45 minutes	→	Eat lunch
4 hours	→	Work on computer
45 minutes	→	Drive home
4 hours	→	Watch TV/Read
14 ¼ hours	→	Total potential sitting time each day

WHAT TO AVOID

In the Living Room
Sitting on a chair and resting a laptop on your lap can negatively impact blood circulation.[192]

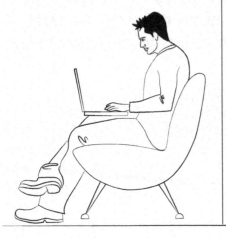

In the Home
Putting cushions behind your back is not enough, since it doesn't achieve the optimal angle between your body and the notebook (which is 90°).

Away from Home
Do not lean over the laptop. It is best to lean back on the chair, but limit the time spent in this position.

Multiple Choice (or Not!)

After reviewing the chapter assignments, circle the correct answer(s) for each of the questions below. (Note – some questions have more than one right answer.)

1. In the United States:
a. 80% of jobs require no physical activity
b. The "average Joe" sits for 9.3 hours per day
c. Office workers sit for an average of 12 hours per day
d. All of the above

2. When a person sits for just 30 minutes:
a. The body becomes less sensitive to insulin
b. Metabolism drops by up to 90%
c. Electrical activity and muscles in the lower body and legs are turned off
d. Brain activity starts to decrease

3. When you sit for 4-6 hours:
a. Risk of death from any cause rises by 50%
b. Nothing bad happens
c. Risk of an adverse cardiovascular event rises by 125%
d. Risk of colon cancer rises by 2X

4. According to Dr. James Levine of Mayo Clinic, sitting:
a. Is more dangerous than smoking
b. Kills more people than HIV
c. Is something we should all do more of
d. Is more treacherous than parachuting

5. The dangerous cluster of diseases related to excessive sitting include:
a. Breast and colon cancers
b. Cardiovascular diseases
c. Diabetes, depression, and dementia
d. Sitting is totally unrelated to disease

6. When we fail to move regularly:
a. Our inactivity leads to abdominal fat
b. Chronic inflammation eventually sets in
c. Our response to threats such as COVID-19 may be impaired
d. All of the above

7. Being active at least 7 hours per week reduces your chances of dying early by:
a. 10% over those who are only active 30 minutes per week
b. 25% over those who are only active 30 minutes per week
c. 40% over those who are only active 30 minutes per week
d. No reduction in risk has been found

8. For most of human history, the preferred position for resting has been:
a. Reclining in an easy chair
b. Lying prone on one's left size
c. Swinging in a hammock
d. Squatting

9. Areas in the world where people tend to live the longest are known as:
a. Green Zones
b. Blue Zones
c. Latitudes of Longevity
d. Centenarian States

10. Researchers have noted that squatting:
a. Utilizes more core muscles than either sitting or standing
b. Translates into healthier hips
c. Improves the health of the spine
d. All the above

11. With regard to exercise:
a. Being a couch potato reduces immune system function
b. Overtraining reduces immune system function
c. Moderate exercise boosts immune system function
d. All of the above

12. In the United States and Europe combined, the number of people who die from adverse reactions to prescription drugs each year is:
a. Negligible
b. An estimated 5,000
c. An estimated 100,000
d. An estimated 328,000

True – or Alternative Fact?

Circle the correct True or False answer for each of the statements below:

1.	Sitting is an independent risk factor for a weak immune system.	True	False
2.	When you sit for 2 hours or more, HDL (good cholesterol) drops by 20%.	True	False
3.	There is no connection between today's sedentary lifestyle and the proliferation of chronic health conditions.	True	False
4.	The adipose tissues of the body produce pro-inflammatory cytokines, which may be one reason why obesity was linked to more severe cases of COVID-19.	True	False
5.	Researchers have found that getting more exercise is one of the slowest ways to improve physical health.	True	False
6.	The ability to squat has been associated with a lower risk of dying over the next six years.	True	False
7.	The ability to easily rise from either a squatting position or sitting on the floor (while touching as few body parts to the ground as possible) has been found to be a predictor of how soon you could die.	True	False
8.	The ability of sustained exercise to create an artificial fever is one of the factors behind the many health benefits of exercise.	True	False
9.	Pharmaceuticals are more effective than exercise at promoting health.	True	False
10.	Exercise-related heart attacks are very common.	True	False

Sitting on Statistics

As explained in Pandemic Busters, sitting is an independent risk factor for a weak immune system. Draw lines to match the potential health impact of the various lengths of times spent sitting:

30 Minutes	Brain activity starts to decrease. Breakdown of dangerous blood fats becomes slower. Electrical activity and muscles in the lower body and legs are turned off.
2 Hours	HDL (good) cholesterol drops by 20%. Metabolism drops by up to 90% as calorie-burning activity plummets. Oxygen consumption levels decrease, making even simple exercises more difficult.
4 Hours	Risk of a cardiovascular event skyrockets by up to 125%. Risk of colon cancer rises by 2X and risk of rectal cancer rises by 44%.
6 Hours	Risk of death from any cause rises by 50%. The body becomes less sensitive to insulin.

Self-Rating Scale

INSTRUCTIONS: Circle the answer that fits you best.

	😄	🙂	🙁	😢
I rarely sit down during the day:	That's true!	I sit down once in a while	I sit quite a bit of the time	I'm almost always sitting
I would describe my posture while sitting as:	Excellent	Pretty good	A bit slouchy	Posture? What posture?
When I do have to sit a lot, I take breaks often to get up and move:	Always!	Most of the time	I'm not very good at that	Never
I frequently sit for more than 4 hours without getting up:	Never!	Very rarely	Quite a bit	All the time!
I can squat very easily, and even get up from a squat:	Of course!	If I worked at it	Not so much	That's impossible!
I have (and regularly use) a standing desk:	Always	Most of the time	Sometimes	Not at all
I really need to sit less and move more, and I'm determined to do it:	I'm up and around a lot already	I do pretty well, but could improve some	I definitely need to do better	This is a huge need in my life!

Review your answers in the previous section. Are there any simple and/or immediate steps you can take to improve in any of these areas? If so, list them below:

Steps I Can Take:

1 _____
_____
_____
_____

2 _____
_____
_____
_____

3 _____
_____
_____
_____

4 _____
_____
_____
_____

5 _____
_____
_____
_____

SESSION 8 / Worksheets
Action Plan

Review the "Action Plan" from chapter 13 as summarized below. Put a check mark by the ones you are ready to work on:

- ○ Consider how much time you spend sitting each day. If it's too much, what could you do to improve?

- ○ If you're physically able, try squatting. Think about how you could add a bit of squatting into your daily routine.

- ○ If you are able to walk at all, get started with a daily walking program, even if that means only walking across the room a few times to start. Use the FITT (Frequency, Intensity, Time, Type) prescription to set-up your plan.

Other Points to Remember

Are there other points you would like to remember from the chapters covered in this session? If so, write them here:

_____

_____

_____

_____

_____

_____

_____

_____

_____

_____

_____

/SESSION 9

Reading Assignments:
Chapter 16: Infection Protection: Lifesaving Things You Should Know
Chapter 10: Adopt a Chinchilla: Not!

What You'll Learn:
At the end of this session, you will have a better understanding of:

Chapter 16:
- How your immune system functions, and why you should care
- How some nasty illnesses (COVID-19 and others) "sneak in" and gain a foothold in the body
- The incredible role of interferons in promoting healthy immune responses
- What a cytokine storm is, how they get started, and what you can do to bolster your defenses against them
- The role of inflammation and comorbidities in cytokine storms
- Why more people are interested in quick fixes than immune-boosting lifestyle strategies
- Key supplements shown to boost immune system function

Chapter 10:
- Why exotic pets are more likely than dogs, cats, and domestic farm animals to carry—and transmit – disease
- What zoonotic disease is, and why it matters to you
- Deadly zoonotic diseases throughout the history of the world
- How scientists (using high tech) can trace the source of disease
- The deadly formula that triggers a worldwide pandemic
- Health benefits of having a cat or a dog as a pet

Bonus Sections:
- Mucus is Your Friend-Here's Why
- How to Keep Your Mucosal Lining – and Other Barriers – Tuned Up.

Worksheets:
- Multiple Choice (or Not!)
- True – or Alternative Fact?
- Supplement Helpers
- Self-Rating Scale
- Steps You Can Take
- Action Plan
- Other Points to Remember

Mucus is Your Friend: Here's Why

Mucus is one of those things people would rather not talk about. The word itself brings up unpleasant memories of stuffy noses and yucky green discharge we'd rather forget. Despite its bad look and even worse rap, mucus plays a vital role in immune system function.[193]

Did you know that your body produces more than a quart (or liter) of new mucus daily?[194] All the wet surfaces of your body that aren't covered by skin (like your eyes, lungs, nose, and mouth) are liberally coated with this gooey stuff, which:

- Is made mostly of water (up to 90%)[195]
- Keeps the delicate tissues of your body from drying and cracking (which protects against infection)[196]
- Lubricates your eyes so you can blink[197]
- Protects your stomach lining from acid[198]
- Houses the trillions of beneficial bacteria that make up your body's microbiome[199]
- Assists the "good guy" bacteria with important functions such as synthesizing vitamins and suppressing inflammation[200]
- Protects the health of the microbiome by keeping the "bad guys," which it traps and neutralizes, under control[201]
- Works like a slimy, continuous conveyer belt to usher bad bacteria, viruses, and pathogens from the body[202]

When the body senses a threat it ramps up mucus production to kill, trap, and remove the invaders. Although mucus is most commonly seen when we are ill, in reality this sticky green substance is just one part of your very complicated, amazing, and powerful immune system.

Your body's defense system has a set of three powerful barriers to protect against invasion and illness from bacteria, viruses, and pathogens. You don't have to be a doctor to understand these barriers. In fact, to best protect your health, you need to. Following is a quick overview of each barrier and what it does:

Barrier #1: Skin and Mucus Lining

These are the physical and chemical defenses, or boundaries, meant to keep trouble out of the body. If you sustain a cut or "breach" to the boundary of your skin, your body will respond with an accumulation of white blood cells which turn yellow as they die (mucus again). Invaders often seek to enter the body through openings in its body surface (such as the eyes, nose, and mouth). As a protective measure, the body tries to cut threats off "at the pass" by lining these areas with mucus.

Barrier #2: The Innate Immune System

The second layer of defense, the innate immune system, is the body's rapid response team. Like an ambulance service, this system is always on standby, ready to spring into action whenever a threat appears.[203] Some of the paramedics on this ambulance team include:

CYTOKINES: When cells within the body are damaged or suffering from injury, the body sends out "help me" signals in the form of what we call cytokines. Several types of these immune system helpers (interleukin-1, interleukin-6, and tumor necrosis factor alpha) are deeply involved in fighting off threats to the body.[204]

COMPLEMENT PROTEINS: As soon as the cytokine "help me" signals roll out, a set of complement proteins speed to the injury site. Their job is to mark the intruders with chemical "eat me" tags which makes the search and destroy mission of the immune system's killer cells much easier.[205]

WHITE BLOOD CELLS: The minute the "help me" alarm is sounded, white blood cells (and other protective, fighting cells such as neutrophils and macrophages) also scurry to the site of the invasion at a high rate of speed. Their job is to kill the intruders, engulf them in "body bags" of mucus, and expel them from the body post haste.[206]

Inflammation (an important disease-related medical buzzword in recent years) is both a physical and chemical reaction that is closely related to the level of cytokines in the blood.[207] When inflammation sets in, that means the body has many cytokine cells crying out "help me!" That is why the level of inflammation is often measured by the presence (and level) of inflammatory cytokines (such as interleukin-1, interleukin-6, and tumor necrosis factor alpha) in the blood.[208]

Barrier #3: The Adaptive Immune System

The third barrier in the immune system, as the name implies, is the part that "adapts" to whatever threat the body is facing. This adaptation is done through the creation of something called antibodies.

Like the innate immune system, the adaptive immune system responds to the "help me" and "eat me" signals by racing to the scene of the crime. Using its amazing ability to create an imprint of the shape of the invader, the adaptive immune system creates antibodies that enable the body to remember and protect against that specific threat in the future.[209]

Three Barriers, Working Together

These three immune system barriers work beautifully together.

1. The first barrier (skin and mucus lining) seeks to keep invaders out.
2. The second barrier, with its white blood cells, "eat me" and "help me" signals, works to kill and expel harmful invaders.
3. The third barrier, with its adaptive and protective powers, creates specifically designed antibodies to ensure that the body will be quickly and more powerfully protected from similar future threats

How to keep Your Mucosal Lining – and Other Barriers – Tuned up

MUCUS IS THE ONLY SUBSTANCE IN THE BODY THAT CAN:
- Fight infections
- Lubricate the body
- Scrub the insides clean, and
- Domesticate an entire population of teeming bacteria.[210]

In order for all of these wonderful functions to happen, however, your body's mucosal linings must maintain the very best chemical makeup, which will allow them to:

- Be permeable as needed for good things (e.g. nutrient absorption), and
- Remain a trap for the "bad guys."[211]

In recent years, researchers have identified the following highly effective strategies for keeping your mucus lining in tip-top, infection-busting shape:

Strategy #1: Enhance your body's proliferation of good gut microbiota.[212]

Some of the best steps you can take in this regard are to eat a variety of whole, plant-based foods (including legumes).[213] Eating low-sugar fermented foods (such as kimchi, sauerkraut, natto, and healthy yogurt) is another way to boost good bacteria in the body.[214] Researchers have documented that people who consume larger amounts of these foods have fewer cytokines crying "help me" in the body, with the result being less inflammation.[215] In a 12-week study involving 36 participants, Stanford researchers found a diet high in low-sugar fermented foods to be highly beneficial to the immune system function.[216] In his podcast, Dr. Andrew Huberman (of Stanford) recommends 2-4 servings of low-sugar fermented foods per day. Dr. John Harvey Kellogg, of the famed Battle Creek Sanitarium, often had patients consume up to a quart of yogurt per day.[217]

Strategy #2: Breathe through your nose.

Whenever possible (unless eating, speaking, or exercising all-out), breathe through your nose. A healthy nasal microbiome provides a much better filter for viruses and bacteria than the mouth.[218] In addition, researchers have reported that regular mouth breathers run a higher risk of infection.[219] If you have trouble breathing through your nose because of chronically collapsed sinuses or a deviated septum, there is good news. The nasal passages, which have some plasticity, can be dilated through constant nose breathing.[220] It will take time, but the result in terms of health will be well worth the effort. **(NOTE:** *If there is something mechanically wrong, professional help may still be required).*

Strategy #3: Tend to the body's microbiota in areas outside the gut and nose, as well.

The body houses a number of other microbiome sites, including one in the eyes, digestive tract, intestines, mouth, rectum, stomach, vagina (in females), and urethra. Each of these interact with the mucosal lining in their specific area. When the microbiome is healthier in every potential "place," the mucosal lining—and ability for the body to defend itself—will be too.

Strategy #4: Avoid touching your eyes (especially after touching other people or surfaces).

The eyes, which we tend to touch subconsciously, are a major entry point for bacteria and viruses into the body.[221] Though we like to think we don't touch our eyes, we often do. Protecting against that natural tendency is why surgical teams often wear goggles. On another note, whenever you wake up with "sleep" in the corner of your eyes, that crust is actually dead bacteria that your body killed during the night (mucus again). Researchers have found that many people touch their eyes within 30 seconds of shaking hands with another person, thus introducing that person's chemicals into the body.[222]

Strategy #5: Implement other basic health-promoting strategies as well.

Excellent nutrition, good sleep, exercise, fresh air, adequate hydration, exposure to sunlight, temperance, and trust in God are all good health-building strategies that:

- Improve the health of the mucosal lining
- Strengthen the body's immune system, and
- Help to deter disease.

Multiple Choice (or Not!)

After reviewing the chapter assignments, circle the correct answer(s) for each of the questions below. (Note – some questions have more than one right answer.)

1. Your immune system:
   a. Works constantly to protect your body against infection, injury and disease
   b. Is equipped with the power not only to protect, but to heal
   c. Can, when working properly, distinguish between "threats" and your body's own tissue
   d. All of the above

2. When the immune system isn't working properly, the body:
   a. May attack its own organs
   b. Doesn't recognize threats
   c. Rallies quickly and fights off the "bug" right away
   d. Isn't prepared to fight off viruses and pathogens

3. Interferons:
   a. Are chemicals the body releases when it perceives a threat
   b. Send signals to the immune system that an attack is underway
   c. Have often been "switched off" by COVID-19
   d. Are sometimes "shut down" in other diseases besides COVID-19

4. When the body's interferon system is shut down:
   a. The immune system is lulled into a false sense of complacency
   b. The body's interferon system kicks in
   c. The infected person feels fine and continues their normal routine
   d. The silent infection grows stronger and stronger

5. A "Cytokine Storm" happens when:
   a. The body's immune system goes into overdrive in an attempt to fight an infection
   b. Uncontrolled levels of cytokines activate too many immune cells, leading to hyperinflammation
   c. The body attacks its own organs, often causing permanent damage
   d. All of the above

6. When the body doesn't have enough interferons:
   a. The response to an infection is delayed
   b. More can be gotten from bats
   c. The inflammatory response, though delayed, eventually ramps up into a "cytokine storm"
   d. None of the above

7. Cytokine storms:
   a. Destroy tissue but not the infection
   b. Annihilate the infection while leaving body tissues intact
   c. Have been documented in cases of influenza, MERS, and SARS—as well as COVID-19
   d. Are more likely to happen to people whose immune systems are already compromised by inflammation

8. In one study, the American Institute of Lifestyle Medicine has documented that the number of hospitalized COVID-19 patients with at least one comorbidity was:
   a. Negligible
   b. At least 5%
   c. Approximately 23.3%
   d. 86.2%

9. People who are vaccinated should:
   a. Not be concerned with COVID-19, since the vaccine takes care of everything
   b. Continue to take optimal care of their bodies
   c. Do what they can to protect and improve immune system function
   d. Continue to get plenty of sleep

10. Supplements that may be helpful in the fight against COVID-19 include:
   a. Zinc and selenium
   b. Melatonin
   c. N-Acetyl Cysteine (NAC)
   d. Vitamin D

11. You can get adequate selenium in the diet by:
   a. Consuming whole grains and seeds
   b. Eating at least one baloney sandwich daily
   c. Eating 1-2 Brazil nuts daily
   d. Its not possible, you have to take a supplement

12 In addition to its sleep-promoting properties, melatonin has been shown to be a natural:
   a. Anti-viral
   b. Anti-virus
   c. Anti-oxidant
   d. Anti-just about everything

True – or Alternative Fact?

Circle the correct True or False answer for each of the statements below:

1.	Exotic pets are more likely to carry a zoonotic disease than a dog or a cat.	True	False
2.	An estimated 25% of all reptiles are Salmonella carriers.	True	False
3.	Diseases that can be transmitted from animals to humans are called "Zoonosis."	True	False
4.	10% of all emerging diseases are of animal origin.	True	False
5.	Thanks to modern technology, scientists are now much more adept at tracking animal disease.	True	False
6.	Bacteria and viruses replicate – and mutate – at an astonishingly fast rate of speed.	True	False
7.	The deadliest pandemics in the history of the world originated in the animal kingdom.	True	False
8.	Having a domestic cat as a pet is not only stressful, but very bad for your health.	True	False
9.	Dog owners tend to have better cardiovascular health than those who don't own dogs.	True	False
10.	Children who are exposed to domestic cats early in life are less likely to have allergies later on.	True	False

Supplement Helpers

Draw lines to match the supplement helpers with the potential benefits of each.

Melatonin	Researchers believe that this trace mineral, may help protect the immune system against harmful virus mutations. You can get the Recommended Daily Allowance (RDA) of this important mineral by eating 1-2 Brazil nuts daily. Whole grains and seeds are also good sources.
N-Acetyl Cysteine (NAC)	Research has shown that the vast majority of COVID-19 fatalities were low on this important nutrient, which helps reduce the risk of a cytokine storm by regulating immune system response.
Selenium	Well-known for its sleep-promoting properties, this supplement is also a natural antiviral, anti-inflammatory, and antioxidant that may be protective against viruses and pathogens.
Vitamin D	This trace mineral helps the immune system to protect against invading viruses and bacteria.
Zinc	A derivative of the L-cysteine (an amino acid), this supplement helps boost glutathione levels, which are important for their immune system support. It is also helpful to the lungs, where it reduces inflammation and inhibits the replication of viruses.

SESSION 9 / Worksheets
Self-Rating Scale
INSTRUCTIONS: Circle the answer that fits you best.

	😊	😐	😟	😢
I'm pretty sure my immune system is in tip-top shape:	Yes	Mostly	That's debatable	Not at all!
My pandemic-related health risk is greater because of other health conditions I have:	Not at all	Perhaps slightly	It's definitely elevated	My risk is much higher
I'm doing all that I can to boost my immune system and make it stronger:	Always	Most of the time	Some of the time	Not really
I have one or more exotic pets in my home:	No	No, but I get exposed elsewhere	Yes, one or two	I've got quite a collection!

_____
_____
_____
_____
_____
_____
_____

Review your answers in the previous section. Are there any simple and/or immediate steps you can take to improve in any of these areas? If so, list them below:

Steps I Can Take:

1 _____

_____

_____

_____

2 _____

_____

_____

_____

3 _____

_____

_____

_____

4 _____

_____

_____

_____

5 _____

_____

_____

_____

Action Plan

**Review the "Action Plan" from chapters 10 and 16 as summarized below.
Put a check mark by the ones you are ready to work on:**

○ Think about the health of your own immune system. Is it functioning as well as you think it could? If not, what could you do to help it work better?

○ Do you have, personally, any underlying conditions or comorbidities that make you more vulnerable to viruses and/or pathogens that might come along? If there are lifestyle choices you can make that would improve your situation, make a plan to get started.

○ If you have been vaccinated and feel the vaccine is a cure-all, consider re-thinking that position and recommitting to doing all you can to make the vaccine more effective.

○ Do some research on the supplements suggested in Chapter 16 to see if any might be helpful in your particular situation.

○ Consider your exposure to exotic pets, and the health dangers it may entail. Think about ways to reduce or eliminate that exposure, and put your plan into action.

○ If you would like a companion pet, consider a cat or a dog.

Other Points to Remember

Are there other points you would like to remember from the chapters covered in this session? If so, write them here:

_____

_____

_____

_____

_____

_____

_____

_____

Reading Assignment:
Chapter 20: Battle the Bulge – The Link Between Excess Pounds and COVID-19

What You'll Learn:
At the end of this session, you will have a better understanding of:

Chapter 20:
- How BMI (Body Mass Index) became a comorbidity for COVID-19
- Other comorbidities connected to obesity
- The connection between obesity and immune system function
- Why thin folks are not off the hook, and what they should know about osteosarcopenic obesity
- How to know if you are overweight or obese
- Top tips for dropping the poundage
- An introduction to the remedies that worked "back then," and an introduction to why they could still help today

Bonus Sections:
- More Tips on "Battling the Bulge"
- The Healthiest Diet in the World (Hint – It Might Not Be What You Think)

Worksheets:
- Multiple Choice (or Not!)
- True – or Alternative Fact?
- Comorbidity Matching
- Self-Rating Scale
- Steps You Can Take
- Action Plan
- Other Points to Remember

More Tips on Battling the Bulge

As discussed in Chapter 20 of Pandemic Busters, researchers have documented a direct link between obesity and COVID-19. In recent months, evidence on that connection has continued to pile up.[223] If there was ever a time when it was dangerous to be obese, now is that time!

Unfortunately, you might also say that if there was ever a time when it was challenging to lose weight, that time is also now. With the many sedentary jobs and entertainment options available today, living life as a couch potato is more tempting than ever. At the same time, fatty foods are inexpensive and just under our noses much of the time. What's a fat-challenged person to do?

Researchers to the Rescue

Fortunately, in addition to documenting the COVID-obesity connection, researchers are also continuously looking into new weight loss ideas. While there's no quick or easy fix for this "growing" problem, all the little things done in the right direction will contribute to eventual success. Nine effective tips for "battling the bulge" were provided in Chapter 20 of Pandemic Busters. Following, based on recent research, are some additional powerful strategies for dropping the pounds:

Strategy #1: Watch What Your Family Watches!

In a U.K. study, researchers found that limiting the hours of TV advertising for high-fat, sugar-packed, and/or salty foods between 5:30 a.m. and 9 p.m. impacted caloric intake enough to reduce the number of:

- Obese children ages 5-17 by 4.6%
- Overweight children in the same age group by 3.6%

The combined results would be 40,000 fewer U.K. children classed as obese and 120,000 fewer overweight.[224] This would be in addition to the benefits reaped by adults not viewing such ads. (Note to parents: While we can't control what advertisers put on TV, we can turn off the switch!)

Strategy #2: Nix the Soda

Although many studies have connected weight gain and drinking pop, a new study takes things one step further. The study, which examined whether leisure time physical activity could mitigate the pound-producing impact of soda, found that it could not.[225] Once again the old adage has been confirmed: "You can't out-exercise a bad diet." In other soda-related studies, scientists found that people who drink:

- Pop and have a genetic predisposition to weight gain will pack on more pounds than others[226]
- A lot of carbonated drinks are more likely to eat a bad diet overall and be overweight[227]
- Sugar-sweetened drinks (such as pop) eaten with a hamburger at meals are primed to pack on more fat than if the two are consumed separately[228]
- Diet soda may have more food cravings (especially women and those who are already obese)[229]

Strategy #3: Steer Clear of Pollution

Colorado researchers recently documented that breathing dirty air is especially bad for gut health. This boosts the risk of obesity, among other maladies. As it turns out, ozone (the culprit behind at least part of Denver's infamous "brown cloud" is particularly harmful. In the study, young people exposed to higher levels of ozone had less microbial diversity in the gut. A greater percentage of study participant's gut bacteria was also of the species associated with obesity and disease.[230]

Strategy #4: Get Out in Nature

In a recent European study, researchers found that getting out in nature reduced both depression and obesity.[231] Trees and green spaces were especially recommended. In other nature-related research:

- An extra 10 trees on a Toronto, Canada city block was found to provide health benefits equal to up to $10,000 in annual income, per resident[232]
- Hospital patients in the United States with a view of trees from their windows were, on average, discharged one day earlier than those without such views[233]

Strategy #5: Eat Avocadoes

Researchers at the University of Illinois have reported that eating an avocado daily may help redistribute belly fat in women toward a healthier profile. In the 12-week study, women who consumed avocado daily had a reduction in visceral abdominal fat (a particularly dangerous type of deep, gel-like fat which has been linked to diabetes, heart disease, and metabolic disorders).[234] In further support of avocadoes, other researchers have documented that regular avocado consumption:

- Improves gut health[235]
- Significantly lowers LDL (bad) cholesterol,[236] and
- Can suppress hunger (when used as a substitute for simple carbohydrates)[237]

The Healthiest Diet in the World
(Hint: It Might Not Be What You Think)

Since the 1300's when Marco Polo first wrote of the vibrant spices and fragrant teas of the Far East, Asian cuisine has been appreciated by many. What many people don't know, however, is that food people call "Asian" has evolved quite a bit over the years.

Dishes on a modern Chinese restaurant menu, for example, might include sweet and sour pork, Peking roast duck, kung pao chicken, dumplings, or fried rice. As history would have it, Asian cuisine changed in some pretty unhealthy ways when Chinese and other immigrants "Americanized" their diet. A measurement of the protein intake of Chinese in the homeland versus Chinese Americans illustrates this well:

Protein Sources: Chinese Mainland vs. Chinese Americans[238]

	Meat and Fish	Grains
China	20%	54%
Chinese Americans	60%	17%

Today, what we think of as Asian food is a far cry from the Rural Asian Diet (RAD) that many Asians used to eat—and in underdeveloped countries still eat—today.

What is the Rural Asian Diet?

The Rural Asian Diet (RAD), which has received some positive press in recent years due to its health-promoting properties, is:

LARGELY PLANT-BASED: Like the Mediterranean Diet, the RAD is largely plant-based. Rice, which still provides 25-80% of the calories in the daily diet of more than two billion Asians, is the core of the RAD. People following a RAD diet often eat two servings of rice per day. Fruit, grains, nuts, vegetables and seeds are also included.

LOW IN FAT: In contrast to the freer use of olive oil associated with the Mediterranean diet, only a small amount of vegetable oil is used in the RAD—making it significantly lower in fat.

LIMITED IN MEAT: In rural areas of China, meat and fish are used very sparingly, almost as condiments. Red meat is eaten once a month, or, if eaten daily, in very small amounts.

LIMITED DAIRY INTAKE: Eggs and poultry products are eaten no more than weekly.

LOW IN PROCESSED FOODS: Breads, whole grains, rice, rice products, and other minimally processed foods are emphasized in the diet.

Benefits of the Rural Asian Diet

In studying more than 10,000 rural Asians, researchers found that these people had (in comparison to people of the Western, industrialized world):

- Extraordinarily low rates of heart disease
- Dramatically lower rates of certain cancers, such as breast and colon cancer
- Significant longevity advantages
- Much lower average cholesterol and blood pressure levels
- Reduced rates of obesity, osteoporosis, and other chronic degenerative diseases[239]

Choosing the Best Diet for You

Although many people thing the Mediterranean Diet is the healthiest in the world, the Rural Asian Diet may just be superior. The lower free fat content, together with a heavy emphasis on plant-based, unprocessed foods, are what put the RAD in a class by itself.

If you would like to try out the Rural Asian Diet for yourself, we recommend that you try a whole foods, plant-based version that is:

- 70% carbohydrates
- 15% fat
- 15% protein, and has
- 15 grams of fiber for every thousand calories consumed.

For the best results, avoid or severely limit sugary foods, salty fare, free fats, and processed foods in general. If you are familiar with the Mediterranean Diet, you could achieve close to the same goal by following a plant-based version of that plan, with very little (if any) free fat.

Multiple Choice (or Not!)

After reviewing the chapter assignments, circle the correct answer(s) for each of the questions below. (Note – some questions have more than one right answer.)

1. The higher the Body Mass Index (BMI), the higher the rate of COVID-related:
   a. Hospitalization
   b. Intensive Care Unit (ICU) admission
   c. Mechanical ventilation
   d. Death

2. 30% of visibly lean people suffer from osteosarcopenic obesity, meaning they are:
   a. Either undermuscled, have low bone density, or both
   b. Considered to be metabolically obese
   c. Afflicted with fatty liver disease
   d. Hiding vast layers of fat under their skin

3. The number of people in the world who were either overweight or obese:
   a. Hasn't changed much in the past 50 years
   b. Rose from 850 million in 1980 to 2.1 billion in 2014
   c. Dropped from 2.1 billion in 1980 to 850 million in 2014
   d. Has plummeted due to world hunger

4. Common diseases or ailments that are caused by obesity include:
   a. Back pain
   b. Arthritis
   c. Nervous twitching
   d. Cancer

5. Stroke and heart disease risk:
   a. Are elevated for the obese
   b. Decrease with Body Mass Index (BMI)
   c. Have nothing to do with obesity
   d. Are higher for people who are thin

6. ACE2 receptors:
   a. Are a protein found on many cell types
   b. Help regulate blood pressure, inflammation, and wound healing
   c. Are out-of-whack in obese persons
   d. All of the above

7. Some of the best breakfast foods for losing weight include:
   a. Half a plate full of raw green veggies
   b. Non-tropical fruit (such as berries) with a low glycemic index
   c. 1-2 jelly doughnuts
   d. Low glycemic-index whole grains such as oatmeal

8. A "nutritional gastric band" recipe meant to curb appetite before a meal includes:
   a. Flax meal
   b. A moderate dose of high fructose corn syrup
   c. Glucomannan
   d. Chia seeds or psyllium husks

9. Foods that are lower on the Glycemic Index (GI) scale:
   a. Help burn fat by reducing insulin levels
   b. Increase satiety and energy levels
   c. Improve mental performance
   d. All of the above

10. Scientists have found a low GI diet to be protective against:
   a. Heart disease and some cancers
   b. Macular degeneration
   c. Adult onset diabetes
   d. Hockey-related soft tissue injuries

11. Benefits of "Intermittent Fasting" (IF) include:
   a. Higher levels of activated growth hormone
   b. Better insulin regulation
   c. More energy
   d. Faster weight loss

12. Benefits of skipping supper include:
   a. Increased stamina
   b. Reduced risk of chronic disease
   c. Bolstered growth hormone production
   d. Reduction in elevated blood glucose and lipid levels

True – or Alternative Fact?

Circle the correct True or False answer for each of the statements below:

1.	Obesity nearly triples the risk of hospitalization from COVID-19.	**True**	**False**
2.	52% of patients hospitalized for COVID-19 were obese.	**True**	**False**
3.	There's nothing we can do to stop the obesity epidemic, since obesity cannot be prevented.	**True**	**False**
4.	Taking a brisk walk outdoors daily is one of the best ways to boost metabolism and overall health.	**True**	**False**
5.	Low fat diets are always a good idea.	**True**	**False**
6.	Deep sleep, which is when the body repairs and heals at night, is helpful in weight loss.	**True**	**False**
7.	Staying hydrated by drinking plenty of water is an excellent weight loss strategy.	**True**	**False**
8.	Many people confuse dehydration with feelings of hunger.	**True**	**False**
9.	Water consumption causes the body to retain toxins.	**True**	**False**
10.	The best weight loss diet would not include free fats (such as margarine, butter, and oil).	**True**	**False**

Comorbidity Matching

Obesity was not the only comorbidity rearing its ugly head during the pandemic. But it was a "big" one. Draw lines to match the appropriate percentages of hospitalized adult COVID-19 patients in the U.S. with the underlying medical conditions they had:

Hypertension	**20%**
Obesity	**3%**
Cardiovascular disease	**52%**
COPD	**14%**
Renal disease	**32%**
Asthma	**56%**

SESSION 10/Worksheets
Self-Rating Scale
INSTRUCTIONS: Circle the answer that fits you best.

	🙂	😐	🙁	😢
Maintaining an ideal body weight is a struggle for me:	Not at all	Maybe a little	Quite a bit	Absolutely!
I struggle with one or more of the comorbidities that raise the risk of severe COVID-19:	No	I'm on the edge	At least one	2 or more
I'm not overweight, but I'm not fit either:	That's not true!	I could be more fit!	That's a true statement	Definitely
My BMI is right where it ought to be:	Of course!	There is room for a little improvement...	There's room for a lot of improvement	Do we have to talk about this?
I love raw veggies and eat plenty of them every day:	All the time	Quite a bit	Once in a while	Hardly ever
Food is a comfort for me:	Not at all	Once in a while	Most of the time	Always
I either limit or avoid free fats (margarine, cooking oil, etc.):	Always	Not as much as I should	Sometimes	Not!
I take daily walks all I can:	Always	Most of the time	Sometimes	No
I get plenty of sleep each night:	Yes	Most of the time	Sometimes	Hardly Ever

Review your answers in the previous section. Are there any simple and/or immediate steps you can take to improve in any of these areas? If so, list them below:

Steps I Can Take:

1 _____

_____

_____

_____

2 _____

_____

_____

_____

3 _____

_____

_____

_____

4 _____

_____

_____

_____

5 _____

_____

_____

_____

Action Plan

Review the "Action Plan" from chapter 20 as summarized below. Put a check mark by the ones you are ready to work on:

- ○ Take stock of your personal health situation. Are you overweight, obese, or metabolically overweight (visually thin but under-muscled or suffering from bone loss)?

- ○ If the answer to any of the above questions is "yes," review this chapter and decide what you can do to get started on the journey towards better health.

- ○ Leap into action!

Other Points to Remember

Are there other points you would like to remember from the chapters covered in this session? If so, write them here:

_____

_____

_____

_____

_____

_____

_____

_____

_____

_____

_____

Reading Assignments:
Chapter 17: Get Out of Your Head: The Magic of Self-Control
Chapter 19: Recover Your Joy: Powerful Steps You Can Take

What You'll Learn:
At the end of this session, you will have a better understanding of:

Chapter 17:
- The importance of self-control to a successful life, but especially during pandemic times
- The difference between self-control and self-regulation
- Benefits of improved self-control
- A 7-step plan to build more self-control

Chapter 19:
- What stress-free and stressful lives both have in common
- Why laughter is still a good medicine, and the science that backs it up
- 7 ways to laugh more
- The health benefits of strong social ties
- Health benefits of unselfishness, altruism, and giving
- The happiness-inducing, immune-boosting benefits of play
- Examples of apparently useless, yet incredibly useful play in the animal kingdom

Bonus Sections:
- Keys to Happiness (and a Meaningful Life)
- Habits for Happier Living
- Elevate Your Happiness Hormones

Worksheets:
- Multiple Choice (or Not!)
- True – or Alternative Fact?
- Animals at Play
- Self-Rating Scale
- Steps You Can Take
- Action Plan
- Other Points to Remember

Keys to Happiness (and a Meaningful Life)

f you have ever studied the "science" of happiness, you may have realized that there are two conflicting views about it in academic circles today:

- The Individualistic Approach, which emphasizes self-care and self-nurture over the needs of others, and
- The Altruistic Approach, which emphasizes sacrifice for the greater purpose (while tending to downplay individuality).

Dr. Martin Seligman (a pioneer in Positive Psychology) developed a systematic theory that seeks to reconcile these two views. In his search to find out what made happy people happy, Dr. Seligman divided happiness into three levels:

THE PLEASANT LIFE: During this stage, which we can get "stuck in", we learn to savor such basic pleasures as companionship, our natural environment, and/or bodily needs.

THE GOOD LIFE: A higher stage of happiness than The Pleasant Life, The Good Life is achieved when, after discovering our unique virtues and strengths, we employ them creatively to enhance our lives.

THE MEANINGFUL LIFE: During this stage, we find a deep sense of fulfillment by applying our unique or "signature" strengths to a purpose greater than ourselves.

To sum it up, Dr. Seligman found that the most satisfied, upbeat people were those who had achieved The Meaningful Life by discovering and using their "signature strengths" in a purpose larger than themselves.[240]

Habits for Happier Living

f you work in the business world, you're probably well aware of "company culture." That culture is a set of shared behaviors, patterns, or way of doing things. In terms of wellbeing, there is a "happiness culture" that people with peace follow as well. Following is a list of "keys" that can all add up to greater levels of happiness, if applied in your life.

In relationships:

1. Be honest and kind
2. Do things for others
3. Avoid social comparisons
4. Speak well of others
5. Listen well
6. Choose friends that lift you up
7. Cultivate relationships

Acceptance:

1. Be patient
2. Be comfortable with who you are
3. Be kind to yourself
4. Look for the good
5. Forgive easily
6. Judge less

Self-care:

1. Eat well
2. Exercise
3. Meditate
4. Drink lots of water
5. Practice healthy sleep habits
6. Show gratitude
7. Choose faith over fear
8. Make the most of now

Resilience:

1. See failure as opportunity
2. Be open-minded
3. Bounce back from mistakes
4. Cultivate self-discipline
5. Don't take opinions to heart
6. Keep learning new things
7. Let go of what can't be changed

The Winning Mindset:

1. Believe in yourself
2. Dream big and set goals
3. Be part of something bigger
4. Smile often
5. Avoid excuses

Elevate Your Happiness Hormones

Dopamine, known as the "reward chemical," plays important roles in motivation, pleasure, and learning.[241] Ways to boost dopamine include:

- Completing a task[242]
- Engaging in self-care activities[243]
- Eating favorite foods[244]
- Celebrating little wins[245]

Serotonin, known as the "mood stabilizer," is needed to help you feel happy, self-confident, and relaxed.[246] Serotonin also has calming properties which can "turn down the dial" on tendencies towards anxiety and/or aggression.[247] Ways to boost serotonin levels include:

- Soaking in some sunlight[248]
- Taking a walk in nature or engaging in some other form of exercise[249]
- Optimizing gut health (since most of the body's serotonin is made in the gut)[250]
- Eating complex carb foods such as veggies, fruits, legumes and whole grains[251]

Oxytocin, known as the "love hormone" because it is seen as the driving force behind attraction and caregiving, can be increased by:

- Playing with a baby or dog[252]
- Doing something nice for someone[253]
- Holding hands[254]
- Hugging your family[255]
- Giving compliments[256]
- Listening to music – or making your own[257]

Endorphins, known as the "pain killers," have been shown to increase pleasure. Useful in overcoming addictions, they may also help to reduce anxiety, depression, and stress.[258] Natural ways to increase endorphins include:

- Laughing out loud[259]
- Applying essential oils (such as lavender)[260]
- Getting 5-10 minutes of sunlight[261]
- Exercise[262]

_____

_____

_____

_____

_____

_____

_____

_____

Multiple Choice (or Not!)

After reviewing the chapter assignments, circle the correct answer(s) for each of the questions below. (Note – some questions have more than one right answer.)

1. Self-control is:
a. An outdated Victorian concept
b. One of the most important qualities needed to live a healthy, happy life
c. A key factor in making the lifestyle changes needed to boost immune system function
d. All of the above

2. People who have good self-control are better able to:
a. Control emotions, desires, impulses and behavior
b. Handle pressure
c. Excel in pickleball tournaments
d. Deal with diverse or challenging personalities

3. Self-control is also sometimes known as:
a. Self-discipline
b. Temperance
c. Intracranial coordination
d. None of the above

4. "With self-discipline, almost anything is possible" were the words of:
a. Queen Victoria
b. Winston Churchill
c. Theodore Roosevelt
d. Bon Jovi

5. Trying to make a lot of lifestyle changes "cold turkey":
a. Is a wonderful idea
b. Should be done on January 1 of each year
c. Doesn't work well for most people
d. All of the above

6. When making a lifestyle change, the best strategies include:
a. Writing a song about whatever change you would like to make
b. Choosing one thing you would really like to change
c. Making sure that "one thing" is both doable and impactful
d. Focus on that "one thing" until its conquered

7. Reasons to make positive lifestyle changes include:
a. Strengthening the immune system
b. Living a longer, healthier life
c. Being there for the people you love
d. Having a strong reason to wake up in the morning

8. Setting a start date for a new goal, and putting it on your calendar, will make:
a. You more likely to fail
b. It more likely that you will follow through on that goal
c. The goal seem more real
d. Feelings of guilt increase

9. Social support for achieving goals can be obtained by:
a. Surrounding yourself with self-disciplined people
b. Encouragement from supportive family and friends
c. Reading books written by people who have reached the goals you are striving for
d. All of the above

10. Lifestyle choices that can enhance your ability to reach personal goals include:
a. Eating healthy and sleeping well
b. Keeping focused on your "whys"
c. Confining binge drinking to the weekends
d. Keeping blood sugar levels stable

11. Practical actions that can help you to reach personal goals include:
a. Removing temptations from your home or office
b. Pairing activities you like to do with those that are less attractive
c. Spreading visual cues around your office or home
d. Building rewards into your plan

12 When you sleep, the two main phases of sleep (REM and non-REM) work together to:
a. Speed the digestive process
b. Spark creativity by finding unrecognized links between facts
c. Increase personal coping skills
d. Create new bone marrow

True – or Alternative Fact?

Circle the correct True or False answer for each of the statements below:

1.	People with better social support are more likely to stick with and accomplish their goals.	True	False
2.	Stress without distress is a much better goal than a stress-free life.	True	False
3.	Having a stress-free life enhances immune system function.	True	False
4.	Too much stress in the life increases cortisol levels and impairs immune system function.	True	False
5.	Hippocrates is said to have died by laughing at his own joke.	True	False
6.	Laughter is actually a form of exercise that increases blood flow to the brain.	True	False
7.	Laughing doesn't burn any calories.	True	False
8.	Strong social ties help to reduce inflammation throughout the body.	True	False
9.	Playing games, which is childish and a waste of time, should not be done by adults.	True	False
10.	Engaging in acts of kindness is beneficial to immune system function.	True	False

Animals at Play

Humans can learn something from many adult animals that regularly engage in playful activities. Draw lines to match the appropriate animal to their favorite activities:

Crocodiles	Flip, jump, blow bubble rings, and make up their own games
Dolphins	Play a game with seashells called "drop catch"
Elephants	Love to slide, toss pebbles, tussle, and play with their food before eating it.
Herring Gulls	Slide down slippery slopes and surf the waves
Sea Otters	Love to throw play punches at each other.
Kangaroos	Waggle their heads and dance

Self-Rating Scale

INSTRUCTIONS: Circle the answer that fits you best.

	:)	:|	:(	:'(
Having—and exercising—self-control is one of my strengths:	Absolutely!	Somewhat	That's questionable	Not at all!
I can stick with changes if I master one at a time:	Yes	With a fair amount of work	I have trouble with this	Not at all
I always set doable goals:	Of course!	Most of the time	Some of the time	Rarely
I take time to think about the "why" behind my goals:	Always	Frequently	Sometimes	Never
I like to put deadlines on my goals:	Absolutely!	Quite a bit	Once in a while	I hate deadlines!
The people I "hang out with" are the kind of people I want to be:	Mostly	Some of the time	Not very often	Never
I'm super stressed out a lot of the time:	That's simply not true!	More than I'd like	Quite a bit	Always!
I find myself laughing quite often:	Yes	Some of the time	Rarely	I hardly ever laugh
I have strong social and/or family ties:	Of course!	With most everyone	There are more bad than good	This is a real struggle for me

Review your answers in the previous section. Are there any simple and/or immediate steps you can take to improve in any of these areas? If so, list them below:

Steps I Can Take:

1 _____

_____

_____

_____

2 _____

_____

_____

_____

3 _____

_____

_____

_____

4 _____

_____

_____

_____

5 _____

_____

_____

_____

SESSION 11 / Worksheets
Action Plan

Review the "Action Plan" from chapters 17 and 19 as summarized below. Put a check mark by the ones you are ready to work on:

○ Scan the chapters you have read thus far in this book. Are there some things you would like to change? If so, is there one thing you feel you could focus on to start?

○ Follow the seven steps in this chapter to form a plan and implement it for the area you wish to improve first.

○ Take some time to consider the stress load in your life. Do you have manageable "good" stress? Or are you "distressed," overloaded, and facing burnout? If the latter is true, think of some baby steps you can take to change.

○ Think about how many times you have laughed in the last week. If you find yourself too burdened to laugh or smile, consider and implement some strategies to begin to find joy again.

○ Even if you are isolated, make efforts to keep social connections alive through phone calls, online groups, or video chats.

○ Schedule a "play night" once a week with family and/or friends.

Other Points to Remember

Are there other points you would like to remember from the chapters covered in this session? If so, write them here:

_____

_____

_____

_____

_____

_____

_____

Reading Assignments:
Chapter 21: Rest from Distress: Finding Your Happy Place During Difficult Times

Chapter 22: Choose Peace: The Power of Hope to Help

What You'll Learn:
At the end of this session, you will have a better understanding of:

Chapter 21:
- Societal increases in depression and anxiety during pandemic times
- The benefits of Cognitive Behavioral Therapy (CBT) in treating the thinking errors associated with depression and anxiety
- 10 common thinking traps and how to avoid them
- Why venting should be out and forgiveness in
- Tips for "making peace with yourself"
- How to re-think your core values

Chapter 22:
- Why what – and how – you think has a direct impact on your immune system function
- The direct connection between optimism and physical health
- The "new" science of psychoneuroimmunology and what it should mean to you
- 6 ways to add more positivity and hopefulness to your life
- Understanding the 10 causative factors for depression
- Why recognizing depression and its causes can be the first step towards healing
- How faith (or lack thereof) impacts health, and what you can do about it

Bonus Sections:
- How to Beat "Sticky" Thoughts
- How Gratitude Changes Your Brain

Worksheets:
- Multiple Choice (or Not!)
- True – or Alternative Fact?
- Stinkin' Thinkin' Matching
- Self-Rating Scale
- Steps You Can Take
- Action Plan
- Other Points to Remember

SESSION 12 / Bonus Section 1
How to Beat "Sticky" Thoughts

Most people now understand that some of the side effects of the pandemic (plus fallout from steps taken to try to contain it) impact the mind. Across the board, levels of anxiety, depression, and stress have risen right along with cases of COVID-19.

Though not as frequently discussed, another mental challenge that some have faced is that of intrusive (or "sticky") thoughts.[263] Intrusive thoughts are unwanted notions or images which, having become "stuck" in the mind, can be difficult to dislodge. People with Obsessive Compulsive Disorder (OCD) struggle with them all the time. At the height of their COVID illness, many normally balanced people have battled them, too.

Pandemic-specific intrusive thoughts might be related to heightened fear, negative thinking, or other OCD tendencies. Whatever the fixation, here are some strategies to consider if your normal thought processes have been disrupted by "sticky" thoughts:

Strategy #1: Label such thoughts for what they are – just thoughts

One of the best things you can do when troubled by intrusive thoughts is to label them for exactly what they are: thoughts. The fact that something passed through your head does not mean you did it! Thoughts are not the same as intent or behavior. (Note: this strategy is not the best if you are struggling with obsessive thoughts of harming yourself or others. In such cases, seek professional help at once.)

Strategy #2: Take care of yourself

You can learn to manage stress better through thoughtful self-care. If your mind is "stuck in a rut," take time out to focus on active coping strategies for managing stress. Such strategies can help reduce the frequency or tendency of unwanted thoughts.

Strategy #3: Try some Cognitive Behavioral Therapy (CBT)

CBT, a research-backed therapy for the mind, seeks to challenge and disrupt negative thought patterns people may have about themselves, others, and the world. Researchers have found CBT to be effective in treating multiple mental health challenges—including anxiety, depression, and obsessive/intrusive thoughts.[264]

CBT utilizes an "ABC" model to help people reshape or replace negative thoughts. That model, which was created by Dr. Albert Ellis, features three important components:

A refers to the initial Adversity or an **Activating Event**

B refers to your **Belief System** about the event and/or the people involved (including yourself)

C refers to the **Consequences** (or your actions in response to that event)

By helping people to understand the relationship between A (the ACTIVATING EVENT) and B (BELIEF SYSTEMS), CBT seeks to alter C (CONSEQUENCES), or how we respond to the event. For example, if your BELIEF SYSTEM assumes that someone is a jerk, all of the ACTIVATING EVENTS related to that person will be interpreted in light of your BELIEF SYSTEM. Your actions in response to virtually anything that person does (CONSEQUENCES) will naturally be impacted by your deeply held beliefs about them.

By challenging B (the BELIEF SYSTEM), CBT seeks to alter C (the CONSEQUENCES, or our response). In other words, by recognizing and making changes in where the "bad thoughts" originate (e.g. a faulty BELIEF SYSTEM), you can alter your response, or the future outcome.

To help people recognize "twisted thinking," CBT divides irrational thoughts into ten categories. (A good summary of these categories is provided in Pandemic Busters. Many good books have also been written on the subject.)

Strategy #4: Focus on the "good judgment" side of your brain

It's been said that there are two sides to our brains:
1. The "smart brain" (where good judgment resides), and
2. The "fear brain."

Your smart brain knows who you are, where you are going, and what you are doing. The fear brain is not smart, however. The side of the brain that deals with threats, the fear brain can't tell the difference between what's imagined and real. The fear brain works really quickly – sometimes when it doesn't need to work at all. During challenging times such as these, the goal should be to listen to what the fear brain says, but let the smart brain do the thinking.

Similar to CBT, this strategy deals with defeating distorted thoughts. In this day and age, there are things to be afraid of, to be sure. But the fear brain should not do our thinking. The smart brain should.

> *"For God hath not given us the spirit of fear; but of power, and of love, and of a sound mind."*
>
> (2 Timothy 1:7, KJV)

How Gratitude Changes Your Brain

In their efforts to help patients get better, mental health professionals are always looking for ways to help patients heal the fastest in the shortest amount of time. In this search, the ideal "activity" for clients would be one that isn't overly taxing but yields high results. One of the most promising activities to emerge from this quest is the practice of gratitude. In recent years, many studies have confirmed that people who consciously count their blessings tend to be happier than those who don't.

IIn addition to promoting happiness, practicing gratitude has also been scientifically proven to:

- Boost the immune system[265]
- Improve mental health[266]
- Strengthen relationships[267]
- Increase optimism[268]
- Improve resilience[269]

Practicing Gratitude

If you haven't been in the habit of practicing gratitude, you might wonder how to get started. Truth is, there are many ways to show gratefulness. Following are some ideas to get you started:

- Keep a "Gratitude Journal"
- Pay attention (be mindful) of the little things in life – like birds singing merrily in the trees
- Thank someone for who they are or what they did – even if it was a long time ago
- Do something kind for someone in your life
- Make a list, or think about, all the good and positive things in your life
- Thank God through prayer

How to Keep a Gratitude Journal

The first strategy mentioned above, keeping a gratitude journal, is one of the best ways to cultivate a positive, even cheery, attitude even during difficult times. Keeping such a journal isn't really that hard. Following are some steps to get you started:

Step #1: Set aside a notebook for the purpose

You may use a computer or an app (if you must). But there is much good to be said about writing things out by hand.

Somehow, it helps the flow of thoughts. The Bible tells us that Jesus once wrote in the sand. (John 8:11) It wasn't gratitude He was writing about. But just to say, sand-writing is Biblical! In any case, find something you want to write on, and get started!

Step #2: Every day, take note of – and write about – at least three positive things that you saw or that happened that day. (When you feel discouraged, reading this journal will help lift your spirits). Ideas to get you started include:

- Something beautiful you saw in nature
- Funny things that made you chuckle today
- Something nice someone said – or did – that touched or uplifted you
- A happy occurrence, event, or bit of news
- Something nice you said or did that helped someone else
- The joy you received from a kitten, puppy, or other beloved pet
- A spiritual nudge or direction you received
- Something fun, fantastic, or meaningful that you did that day

If you like, you may find it beneficial to focus your journal on an area you really want to improve in your life. Not to worry – you can still be positive about them! For example:

- If you're struggling with feelings of worthlessness, write about three things you can be proud of or delight in.
- If a rocky relationship is challenging you, write about three good things you saw in your "difficult person" today.
- If you want to improve your relationship with God, write about three ways you saw His hand in your life today. (Some people call this their "Tender Mercies" journal).
- If your job is a major problem, write about three things that happened at work that you are thankful for.

If still looking for "gratitude inspiration," you might try reading the Bible—especially the psalms. There are many inspiring verses about gratitude and thankfulness in its pages. Here are a few to get you started:

- **"Give thanks in all circumstances; for this is the will of God in Christ Jesus for you."** (1 Thessalonians 5:18)
- **"This is the day that the Lord has made; let us rejoice and be glad in it."** (Psalm 118:24)

Multiple Choice (or Not!)

After reviewing the chapter assignments, circle the correct answer(s) for each of the questions below. (Note – some questions have more than one right answer.)

1. The words "I have learned in whatsoever state I am therewith to be content" were said by:
a. Judas Iscariot
b. Paul the Apostle
c. Pontius Pilate
d. Benedict Arnold

2. Psychiatric medicines such as benzodiazepines, SSRIs, antipsychotic meds, and stimulants:
a. Have been freely used to treat pandemic-related anxiety and depression
b. Create neurotransmitter imbalances in the brain
c. Often lead to dependence on drugs
d. All of the above

3. Cognitive Behavioral Therapy (CBT):
a. Has helped many people change their thought patterns by taking responsibility for their thinking
b. Can help people to have better relationships
c. Is beneficial in grief recovery
d. Is useful in many situations

4. People who engage in the "black and white" or polarized thinking error:
a. See everything in absolutes
b. Have their extreme thinking fed by search engine and social media
c. Respect the viewpoints of others
d. Leave no room for opposing points of view

5. People who engage in the thinking error of "sweeping generalizations":
a. Draw major conclusions based on a single experience
b. Are prone to anxiety disorders and PTSD
c. Are usually right in their assumptions
d. Poll others before forming opinions

6. People who commit the "mental filter" thinking error:
a. Tend to look at life through a filter that sees what they want to see
b. May suffer from anxiety or depression
c. Are generally the happy-go-lucky sort
d. May engage in suicidal thoughts

7. People who commit the thinking error of "explaining away the positives":
a. Do see positive things, but explain them away
b. Often assume that good outcomes are only a fluke
c. Feel they have no control over circumstances
d. Are often lacking in motivation

8. People who engage in the thinking errors of magnification or minimization:
a. Inaccurately exaggerate or minimize the importance of life events
b. May blow things out of proportion
c. May ignore important problems
d. All of the above

9. Emotional reasoners:
a. Rely on logic and statistics to form their opinions
b. Often rely on gut feelings to make major decisions
c. Are usually extremely energetic people
d. Are more likely to be lazy

10. The thinking error of personalization has been linked to people:
a. Blaming themselves for things that aren't their fault
b. Believing that they are being intentionally targeted—or excluded—when they aren't
c. Healthy and well-deserved feelings of guilt
d. Feelings of inappropriate guilt

11. Studies have shown that people with more optimism tend to have:
a. Stronger immune systems overall
b. Higher levels of immune protective cells such as antibodies and T cells
c. Lower blood pressure and triglycerides
d. Elevated blood pressure and triglycerides

12. Successful strategies for being a more positive person include:
a. Pepping up posture and body language
b. Nixing the negative words and phrases
c. Making a gratitude list
d. Drinking eggnog at least once a day

True – or Alternative Fact?

Circle the correct True or False answer for each of the statements below:

1.	The COVID-19 pandemic significantly increased the levels of anxiety and depression in the United States.	**True**	**False**
2.	A family history of suicide or depression is one of the ten "hit" factors that could predispose you to depression yourself.	**True**	**False**
3.	Sleep deprivation has nothing to do with depression.	**True**	**False**
4.	Regularly going against one's conscience can lead to depressed thoughts.	**True**	**False**
5.	Listening to rap music is one of the best cures for depression.	**True**	**False**
6.	Hydrotherapy (or hot and cold treatments) can treat depression by stimulating blood flow to the brain.	**True**	**False**
7.	Regular physical exercise can be very depressing.	**True**	**False**
8.	Researchers have found daily spiritual exercise (such as Bible study and prayer) to be helpful in treating depression.	**True**	**False**
9.	40-50% of U.S. medical patients say that faith is helpful to them in their fight against illness.	**True**	**False**
10.	Bible-believing Christians have been found to have more optimism when confronting illness than those from more liberal religious traditions.	**True**	**False**

Stinkin' Thinkin' Matching

One of the goals of Cognitive Behavioral Therapy (CBT) is to straighten out thinking errors, or "stinkin' thinkin'" as it is sometimes called. Match each kind of thinking error with the example that fits:

Black & White (Polarized) Thinking	One negative event is used to draw important conclusions
Sweeping Generalizations	Good things are seen, but explained as "flukes"
Mental Filters	One characteristic of a person is used to define the entire person
Explaining Away the Positives	People think they know the future before it arrives
Mind Reading	One way or another, people blow things way out of proportion
Fortune Teller Error	People rely on gut feelings to make major decisions
Maximization or Minimization	Everything is seen in absolutes (e.g. black and white, good and evil)
Emotional Reasoning	Slights or events that aren't connected to a person at all are taken very personally by them
Labeling	People assume they know what others are thinking
Personalization	We see what we set out to see

SESSION 12/Worksheets
Self-Rating Scale

INSTRUCTIONS: Circle the answer that fits you best.

	😊	🙁	🙁	😢
I see most things in life as pretty much simple, in black and white:	Some are, but some are not	There are a lot of gray areas	Everything is a gray area to me	Yes
I can usually tell what other people are thinking:	No	Not that well	Pretty much	Absolutely!
I never exaggerate:	Is that a trick question?	Not usually	Once in a while	All the time (like right now!)
I'm pretty good at guessing future events:	No	Not very	Somewhat	Definitely!
It really does seem like people are out to get me, most of the time:	No	Once in a while	Most of the time	Always!
The way I live is in sync with my core values:	Most of the time	Some of the time	Rarely	Not really
Others see me as a very positive person:	Most of the time	Some of the time	Rarely	Hardly ever
I struggle with anxiety and/or depression:	Not really	Once in a while	Some of the time	Most of the time
My faith is strong; I know that God can handle the future:	Absolutely!	Most of the time	Some of the time	Not so much

Review your answers in the previous section. Are there any simple and/or immediate steps you can take to improve in any of these areas? If so, list them below:

Steps I Can Take:

1 _____

_____

_____

2 _____

_____

_____

3 _____

_____

_____

4 _____

_____

_____

5 _____

_____

_____

_____

Action Plan

Review the "Action Plan" from chapters 21 and 22 as summarized below.
Put a check mark by the ones you are ready to work on:

○ If you have navigated through the pandemic with the help of prescription drugs or self-medicated with alcohol, recreational drugs or some other diversion, consider how to replace those stress-management mechanisms with healthier habits.

○ Consider the list of 10 thinking errors in light of your own life. If you honestly feel you have slipped into one or more of those errors, try to see the big picture and straighten out your thinking.

○ If you are struggling with anxiety or depression or feel like you might have fallen into some thinking errors, consider reading a good book on CBT. If you are really in trouble, please seek help at once.

○ Think of some times you have "vented." Has the outcome usually been good? If not, consider how you could improve your response to challenging situations.

○ Follow the steps in the book under the heading "How to Re-think Your Core Values." If there is stress or dissonance in your life caused by a gap between what you believe and how you are living, make a plan for how to relieve that stress.

○ Review the ways (in Chapter 22) to be a more hopeful and positive person. If you haven't been practicing those mood-boosting strategies in your life, decide which one(s) to try, and get started.

○ Consider the lifestyle choices in Chapter 22 as well, and try out one or more that you think might be helpful to you.

○ Re-read the list of "Hits" that trigger depression. Consider the ones you have control over, and how you can use those to reduce your risk of depression.

○ If you aren't already, try reading a Bible passage from Proverbs every day for a week. We also recommend looking up some of the many texts where the Bible uses the words "Fear not" or "Do not be afraid."

○ Try bringing your troubles to God. "Casting all your care upon Him, for He careth for you." (1 Peter 5:7)

Other Points to Remember

Are there other points you would like to remember from the chapters covered in this session? If so, write them here:

_____

_____

1　Armstrong JF. When the flu killed millions. RN. 1999 Dec 1;62(12):32-.

2　Wheelock DC. What Can We Learn from the Spanish Flu Pandemic of 1918-19 for COVID-19? Federal Reserve Bank of St. Louis Economic Synopses. 2020 May;30:1-4.

3　Ibid.

4　Wilton P. Spanish flu outdid WWI in number of lives claimed. CMAJ: Canadian Medical Association Journal. 1993 Jun 1;148(11):2036.

5　Simonsen L, Clarke MJ, Schonberger LB, Arden NH, Cox NJ, Fukuda K (July 1998). "Pandemic versus epidemic influenza mortality: a pattern of changing age distribution". The Journal of Infectious Diseases. 178 (1): 53–60.

6　https://www.alaskapublic.org/2020/05/06/what-alaskans-learned-from-the-mother-of-all-pandemics-in-1918/.

7　Hobday RA, Cason JW. The open-air treatment of pandemic influenza. American journal of public health. 2009 Oct;99(S2):S236-42.

8　https://virus.stanford.edu/uda/.

9　Schoch-Spana M. "Hospitals full-up": the 1918 influenza pandemic. Public Health Reports. 2001;116(Suppl 2):32.

10　Ibid.

11　Cipriano PF. 100 years on: the Spanish flu, pandemics and keeping nurses safe. International nursing review. 2018 Sep;65(3):305.

12　L. E. Elliott, "The Value of Sanitarium Treatment in Respiratory Diseases," Life & Health Magazine, May, 1919: Vol. 34.

13　Ansello EF. Blue Zones and Longevity.

14　Ahlheim H. Governing the World of Wakefulness: The Exploration of Alertness, Performance, and Brain Activity with the Help of "Stay-Awake-Men"(1884–1964). Anthropology of Consciousness. 2013 Sep;24(2):117-36.

15　VonRueden K. Sleep Deprivation in the Workplace: The Hidden Side of Health and Wellness. InASSE Professional Development Conference and Exposition 2014 Jun 8. OnePetro.

16　Rico-Rosillo MG, Vega-Robledo GB. Sleep and immune system. Revista Alergia Mexico. 2018 Jun;65(2):160-70.

17　Fang HF, Miao NF, Chen CD, Sithole T, Chung MH. Risk of cancer in patients with insomnia, parasomnia, and obstructive sleep apnea: a nationwide nested case-control study. Journal of Cancer. 2015;6(11):1140.

18　Hillman DR. Sleep loss in the hospitalized patient and its influence on recovery from illness and operation. Anesthesia & Analgesia. 2021 May 1;132(5):1314-20.

19　Lange T, Dimitrov S, Born J. Effects of sleep and circadian rhythm on the human immune system. Annals of the New York Academy of Sciences. 2010 Apr;1193(1):48-59.

20　Krueger JM, Obál Jr F, Fang J, Kubota T, Taishi P. The role of cytokines in physiological sleep regulation. Annals of the New York Academy of Sciences. 2001 Mar;933(1):211-21.

21　Werner S, Grose R. Regulation of wound healing by growth factors and cytokines. Physiological reviews. 2003 Jul;83(3):835-70.

22　Westermann J, Lange T, Textor J, Born J. System consolidation during sleep–a common principle underlying psychological and immunological memory formation. Trends in neurosciences. 2015 Oct 1;38(10):585-97.

23　Hillman DR. Sleep loss in the hospitalized patient and its influence on recovery from illness and operation. Anesthesia & Analgesia. 2021 May 1;132(5):1314-20.

24　Dua S, Dowey J, Garcia MR, Bond S, Durham S, Kimber I, Mills C, Roberts G, Skypala I, Wason J, Ewan P. How Reaction Severity Is Affected By Cofactors And Repeat Challenges: A Prospective Study Of Peanut Allergic Adults. Journal of Allergy and Clinical Immunology. 2020 Feb 1;145(2):AB182.

25　Benedict C, Cedernaes J. Could a good night's sleep improve COVID-19 vaccine efficacy?. The Lancet Respiratory Medicine. 2021 May 1;9(5):447-8.

26　Mannino G, Caradonna F, Cruciata I, Lauria A, Perrone A, Gentile C. Melatonin reduces inflammatory response in human intestinal epithelial cells stimulated by interleukin-1β. Journal of pineal research. 2019 Oct;67(3):e12598.

27　Bandyopadhyay A, Sigua NL. What is sleep deprivation?. American journal of respiratory and critical care medicine. 2019 Mar 15;199(6):P11-2.

28　Luxwolda M, Havekes R. Mechanisms of increased infection risk by sleep deprivation. Neurobiology. 2021 Sep.

29　Story of Malcolm Macintosh, as provided by his grandson, Don Macintosh.

30　Petrofsky J, Laymon M, Donatelli R. A comparison of moist heat, dry heat, chemical dry heat and icy hot for deep tissue heating and changes in tissue blood flow. Medical Research Archives. 2021 Jan 28;9(1).

31　Kluger MJ. 4. The Adaptive Value of Fever. In: Fever: Its Biology, Evolution, and Function. Princeton University Press; 2015. p. 129–66.

32　Fusheng YA. Look on the Bright Side of Fever 2019;1.

33　Gumdal GN. Pathophysiology of fever. From the Editor's Desk.:7.

34　Ibid.

35　Plaza JJG, et al. Role of metabolism during viral infections, and crosstalk with the innate immune system. Intractable Rare Dis Res. 2016 May;5(2):90–6.

36　Wrotek S, LeGrand EK, Dzialuk A, Alcock J. Let fever do its job: the meaning of fever in the pandemic era. Evolution, medicine, and public health. 2021;9(1):26-35.

37　Ibid.

38　Ibid.

39　Hu B, Huang S, Yin L. The cytokine storm and COVID-19. Journal of medical virology. 2021 Jan;93(1):250-6.

40　Ramirez FE, Sanchez A, Pirskanen AT. Hydrothermotherapy in prevention and treatment of mild to moderate cases of COVID-19. Medical hypotheses. 2021 Jan 1;146:110363.

41 Paterson C, Gobel B, Gosselin T, Haylock PJ, Papadopoulou C, Slusser K, Rodriguez A, Pituskin E. Oncology nursing during a pandemic: critical reflections in the context of COVID-19. In Seminars in Oncology Nursing 2020 Jun 1 (Vol. 36, No. 3, p. 151028). WB Saunders.

42 Ibid.

43 Del Rio C, Omer SB, Malani PN. Winter of Omicron—The Evolving COVID-19 Pandemic. JAMA. 2021 Dec 22.

44 Meng X, Deng Y, Dai Z, Meng Z. COVID-19 and anosmia: A review based on up-to-date knowledge. American journal of otolaryngology. 2020 Sep 1;41(5):102581.

45 Pinto JM, Wroblewski KE, Kern DW, Schumm LP, McClintock MK. Olfactory dysfunction predicts 5-year mortality in older adults. PloS one. 2014 Oct 1;9(10):e107541.

46 Conti MZ, Vicini-Chilovi B, Riva M, Zanetti M, Liberini P, Padovani A, Rozzini L. Odor identification deficit predicts clinical conversion from mild cognitive impairment to dementia due to Alzheimer's disease. Archives of Clinical Neuropsychology. 2013 Aug 1;28(5):391-9.

47 Yang HJ, LoSavio PS, Engen PA, Naqib A, Mehta A, Kota R, Khan RJ, Tobin MC, Green SJ, Schleimer RP, Keshavarzian A. Association of nasal microbiome and asthma control in patients with chronic rhinosinusitis. Clinical & Experimental Allergy. 2018 Dec;48(12):1744-7.

48 Lee KJ, Park CA, Lee YB, Kim HK, Kang CK. EEG signals during mouth breathing in a working memory task. International Journal of Neuroscience. 2020 May 3;130(5):425-34.

49 Kumpitsch C, Koskinen K, Schöpf V, Moissl-Eichinger C. The microbiome of the upper respiratory tract in health and disease. BMC biology. 2019 Dec;17(1):1-20.

50 Xydakis MS, Albers MW, Holbrook EH, Lyon DM, Shih RY, Frasnelli JA, Pagenstecher A, Kupke A, Enquist LW, Perlman S. Post-viral effects of COVID-19 in the olfactory system and their implications. The Lancet Neurology. 2021 Sep 1;20(9):753-61.

51 De Boeck I, van den Broek MF, Allonsius CN, Spacova I, Wittouck S, Martens K, Wuyts S, Cauwenberghs E, Jokicevic K, Vandenheuvel D, Eilers T. Lactobacilli have a niche in the human nose. Cell Reports. 2020 May 26;31(8):107674.

52 Kumpitsch C, Koskinen K, Schöpf V, Moissl-Eichinger C. The microbiome of the upper respiratory tract in health and disease. BMC biology. 2019 Dec;17(1):1-20.

53 De Boeck I, van den Broek MF, Allonsius CN, Spacova I, Wittouck S, Martens K, Wuyts S, Cauwenberghs E, Jokicevic K, Vandenheuvel D, Eilers T. Lactobacilli have a niche in the human nose. Cell Reports. 2020 May 26;31(8):107674.

54 Savin Z, Kivity S, Yonath H, Yehuda S. Smoking and the intestinal microbiome. Archives of microbiology. 2018 Jul;200(5):677-84.

55 Xydakis MS, Albers MW, Holbrook EH, Lyon DM, Shih RY, Frasnelli JA, Pagenstecher A, Kupke A, Enquist LW, Perlman S. Post-viral effects of COVID-19 in the olfactory system and their implications. The Lancet Neurology. 2021 Sep 1;20(9):753-61.

56 Kataria J. Text Neck–Its Effects on Posture. International Journal of Creative Research Thoughts. 2018;6(1):817-9.

57 Goto Y, Hu A, Yamaguchi T, Suetake N, Kobayashi H. The Influence of a Posture on the Autonomic Nervous System and Stress Hormones in Saliva. Health. 2020 Jan 21;12(2):118-26.

58 Albarrati A, Zafar H, Alghadir AH, Anwer S. Effect of upright and slouched sitting postures on the respiratory muscle strength in healthy young males. BioMed research international. 2018 Feb 25;2018.

59 Zahari Z, Zainudin NF, Justine M. Posture and its relationship with falls among older people with low back pain: A systematic review. Healthscope: The Official Research Book of Faculty of Health Sciences, UiTM. 2020 Jun 30;3(2):13-8.

60 Newitt J, Strollo P. Breathing Problems in Adults with Neuromuscular Weakness. American Journal of Respiratory and Critical Care Medicine. 2020 Dec 1;202(11):P31-2.

61 Metin OI, Caglayan O, Julio L. Human Leptin Deficiency Caused by a Missense Mutation: Multiple Endocrine Defects, Decreased Sympathetic Tone, and Immune System Dysfunction Indicate New Targets for Leptin Action, Greater Central than Peripheral Resistance to the Effects of Leptin, and Spontaneous Correction of Leptin-Mediated Defects, The Journal of Clinical Endocrinology & Metabolism. 1999, October l; 3686–3695.

62 Egan, M. Posture: Health matters. LSJ: Law Society of NSW Journal, 2014;(4), 52.

63 McCrae CS, Lichstein KL. Secondary insomnia: Diagnostic challenges and intervention opportunities.Sleep Medicine Reviews. 2001; 5(1) 47-61.

64 Bradley H, Esformes J. Breathing pattern disorders and functional movement. Int J Sports Phys Ther. 2014;9(1):28-39.

65 H mmig O. Work- and stress-related musculoskeletal and sleep disorders among health professionals: a cross-sectional study in a hospital setting in Switzerland. BMC Musculoskelet Disord 2020;(21):319.

66 Akulwar-Tajane I, Darvesh M, Ghule M, Deokule S, Deora B, Mhatre V. Effects of COVID-19 pandemic lock down on posture in physiotherapy students: a cross-sectional study. Medical & Clinical Research. 2021;6(1):91-102.

67 Szczygieł E, Blaut J, Zielonka-Pycka K, Tomaszewski K, Golec J, Czechowska D, Masłoń A, Golec E. The impact of deep muscle training on the quality of posture and breathing. Journal of motor behavior. 2018 Mar 4;50(2):219-27.

68 Kattenstroth JC, Kalisch T, Holt S, Tegenthoff M, Dinse HR. Six months of dance intervention enhances postural, sensorimotor, and cognitive performance in elderly without affecting cardio-respiratory functions. Frontiers in aging neuroscience. 2013 Feb 26;5:5.

69 Ganesh A, Stahnisch FW. A history of multiple sclerosis investigations in Canada between 1850 and 1950. Canadian Journal of Neurological Sciences. 2014 May;41(3):320-32.

70 Beckett JM, Bird ML, Pittaway JK, Ahuja KD. Diet and multiple sclerosis: scoping review of web-based recommendations. Interactive journal of medical research. 2019 Jan 9;8(1):e10050.

71 Gibson GR, Roberfroid MB. Dietary modulation of the human colonic microbiota: introducing the concept of prebiotics. The Journal of nutrition. 1995 Jun 1;125(6):1401-12.

72   Pollan M. Some of my best friends are germs. New York Times Magazine. 2013 May 15;15.

73   Popkin BM, Ng SW. The nutrition transition to a stage of high obesity and noncommunicable disease prevalence dominated by ultra-processed foods is not inevitable. Obesity Reviews. 2022 Jan;23(1):e13366.

74   Saini P, Kumar N, Kumar S, Mwaurah PW, Panghal A, Attkan AK, Singh VK, Garg MK, Singh V. Bioactive compounds, nutritional benefits and food applications of colored wheat: A comprehensive review. Critical Reviews in Food Science and Nutrition. 2021 Oct 28;61(19):3197-210.

75   Pollan M. Unhappy meals. The New York Times. 2007 Jan 28;28.

76   Clark JA, Coopersmith CM. Intestinal crosstalk–a new paradigm for understanding the gut as the "motor" of critical illness. Shock (Augusta, Ga.). 2007 Oct;28(4):384.

77   Anderson J. Easter Candy Lists 2015.

78   Kong F, Cai Y. Study insights into gastrointestinal cancer through the gut microbiota. BioMed Research International. 2019 Jun 24;2019.

79   Rastelli M, Knauf C, Cani PD. Gut microbes and health: a focus on the mechanisms linking microbes, obesity, and related disorders. Obesity. 2018 May;26(5):792-800.

80   Dhir A. HAPPY GUT, HEALTHY WEIGHT.

81   Johnson KV. Gut microbiome composition and diversity are related to human personality traits. Human Microbiome Journal. 2020 Mar 1;15:100069.

82   Liu RT, Rowan-Nash AD, Sheehan AE, Walsh RF, Sanzari CM, Korry BJ, Belenky P. Reductions in anti-inflammatory gut bacteria are associated with depression in a sample of young adults. Brain, behavior, and immunity. 2020 Aug 1;88:308-24.

83   Gagliardi A, Totino V, Cacciotti F, Iebba V, Neroni B, Bonfiglio G, Trancassini M, Passariello C, Pantanella F, Schippa S. Rebuilding the gut microbiota ecosystem. International journal of environmental research and public health. 2018 Aug;15(8):1679.

84   García López R. Study of the virome and microbiome associated to the proliferative verrucous leukoplakia.

85   Schwartz B, Schwartz B. The paradox of choice: Why more is less. New York: Ecco.

86   Chen J, Ying GG, Deng WJ. Antibiotic residues in food: extraction, analysis, and human health concerns. Journal of Agricultural and Food Chemistry. 2019 Jun 14;67(27):7569-86.

87   Wu Z. Antibiotic use and antibiotic resistance in food-producing animals in China.

88   Barton MD. Antibiotic use in animal feed and its impact on human health. Nutrition research reviews. 2000 Dec;13(2):279-99.

89   Dolliver H, Kumar K, Gupta S. Sulfamethazine uptake by plants from manure-amended soil. Journal of environmental quality. 2007 Jul;36(4):1224-30.

90   Islam MS. Use of bioslurry as organic fertilizer in Bangladesh agriculture. In Prepared for the presentation at the international workshop on the use of bioslurry domestic biogas programme. Bangkok, Thailand 2006 Sep 27 (pp. 3-16).

91   Atolani O, Baker MT, Adeyemi OS, Olanrewaju IR, Hamid AA, Ameen OM, Oguntoye SO, Usman LA. COVID-19: Critical discussion on the applications and implications of chemicals in sanitizers and disinfectants. EXCLI journal. 2020;19:785.

92   Manohar P, Loh B, Leptihn S. Will the overuse of antibiotics during the coronavirus pandemic accelerate antimicrobial resistance of bacteria? Infectious Microbes & Diseases. 2020 Sep 1;2(3):87-8.

93   Livermore DM. Antibiotic resistance during and beyond COVID-19. JAC-antimicrobial resistance. 2021 Jun; 3(Supplement_1) 15-16.

94   Vaughn VM, Gandhi TN, Petty LA, Patel PK, Prescott HC, Malani AN, Ratz D, McLaughlin E, Chopra V, Flanders SA. Empiric antibacterial therapy and community-onset bacterial coinfection in patients hospitalized with coronavirus disease 2019 (COVID-19): a multi-hospital cohort study. Clinical Infectious Diseases. 2021 May 15;72(10):e533-41.

95   Uetrecht J. Immune-mediated adverse drug reactions. Chemical research in toxicology. 2009 Jan 19;22(1):24-34.

96   Long H, Zhao H, Chen A, Yao Z, Cheng B, Lu Q. Protecting medical staff from skin injury/disease caused by personal protective equipment during epidemic period of COVID-19: experience from China. Journal of the European Academy of Dermatology and Venereology. 2020 May;34(5):919.

97   Munyua PM, Njenga MK, Osoro EM, Onyango CO, Bitek AO, Mwatondo A, Muturi MK, Musee N, Bigogo G, Otiang E, Ade F. Successes and challenges of the One Health approach in Kenya over the last decade. BMC public health. 2019 May;19(3): 1-9.

98   Wagner N. Indirect health effects due to COVID-19: An exploration of potential economic costs for developing countries. InCOVID-19 and International Development 2022 (pp. 103-118). Springer, Cham.

99   MacIntyre CR, Bui CM. Pandemics, public health emergencies and antimicrobial resistance-putting the threat in an epidemiologic and risk analysis context. Archives of Public Health. 2017 Dec;75(1):1-6.

100   Murray CJ, Ikuta KS, Sharara F, Swetschinski L, Aguilar GR, Gray A, Han C, Bisignano C, Rao P, Wool E, Johnson SC. Global burden of bacterial antimicrobial resistance in 2019: a systematic analysis. The Lancet. 2022 Jan 19.

101   Eftimov T, Popovski G, Petković M, Seljak BK, Kocev D. COVID-19 pandemic changes the food consumption patterns. Trends in food science & technology. 2020 Oct 1;104: 268-72.

102   Wiemer L. Impact of Tailored Messages to Change Towards a Plant-Based Diet: Media Effects, Behavioral Change and Practical Implications (Doctoral dissertation, Ohio University).

103   Orlich MJ, Fraser GE. Vegetarian diets in the Adventist Health Study 2: a review of initial published findings. The American journal of clinical nutrition. 2014 Jul 1;100(suppl_1):353S-8S.

104   Shen J, Wilmot KA, Ghasemzadeh N, Molloy DL, Burkman G, Mekonnen G, Gongora MC, Quyyumi AA, Sperling LS. Mediterranean dietary patterns and cardiovascular health. Annual review of nutrition. 2015 Jul 17;35:425-49.

105   Bazargan M. Self-reported sleep disturbance among African-American elderly: the effects of depression, health status, exercise, and social support. The International Journal of Aging and Human Development. 1996 Mar;42(2):143-60.

106 Härlein J, Dassen T, Halfens RJ, Heinze C. Fall risk factors in older people with dementia or cognitive impairment: a systematic review. Journal of advanced nursing. 2009 May;65(5):922-33.

107 Rambhade S, Chakarborty A, Shrivastava A, Patil UK, Rambhade A. A survey on polypharmacy and use of inappropriate medications. Toxicology international. 2012 Jan;19(1):68.

108 Pham-Huy LA, He H, Pham-Huy C. Free radicals, antioxidants in disease and health. International journal of biomedical science: IJBS. 2008 Jun;4(2):89.

109 Carrero JJ, González-Ortiz A, Avesani CM, Bakker SJ, Bellizzi V, Chauveau P, Clase CM, Cupisti A, Espinosa-Cuevas A, Molina P, Moreau K. Plant-based diets to manage the risks and complications of chronic kidney disease. Nature Reviews Nephrology. 2020 Sep;16(9):525-42.

110 Iddir M, Brito A, Dingeo G, Fernandez Del Campo SS, Samouda H, La Frano MR, Bohn T. Strengthening the immune system and reducing inflammation and oxidative stress through diet and nutrition: considerations during the COVID-19 crisis. Nutrients. 2020 Jun;12(6):1562.

111 McCarrison R. Studies in Deficiency Disease. Studies in Deficiency Disease. 1921.

112 Campbell JD. Lifestyle, minerals and health. Medical hypotheses. 2001 Nov 1;57(5):521-31.

113 Nayak B, Berrios JD, Tang J. Impact of food processing on the glycemic index (GI) of potato products. Food Research International. 2014 Feb 1;56:35-46.

114 Housekeeper FY, More SM. Nutrition Health Review-Winter 2019. Nutrition. 2019.

115 Etemadian Y, Ghaemi V, Shaviklo AR, Pourashouri P, Mahoonak AR, Rafipour F. Development of animal/plant-based protein hydrolysate and its application in food, feed and nutraceutical industries: State of the art. Journal of Cleaner Production. 2021 Jan 1;278:123219.

116 Palmer BF, Colbert G, Clegg DJ. Potassium homeostasis, chronic kidney disease, and the plant-based diet. Kidney360. 2020 Jan 1:10-34067.

117 Awuchi CG, Igwe VS, Amagwula IO. Nutritional diseases and nutrient toxicities: A systematic review of the diets and nutrition for prevention and treatment. International Journal of Advanced Academic Research. 2020;6(1):1-46.

118 Lima GP, Vianello F. Review on the main differences between organic and conventional plant-based foods. International Journal of Food Science & Technology. 2011 Jan;46(1):1-3.

119 Lacour C, Seconda L, Allès B, Hercberg S, Langevin B, Pointereau P, Lairon D, Baudry J, Kesse-Guyot E. Environmental impacts of plant-based diets: how does organic food consumption contribute to environmental sustainability? Frontiers in nutrition. 2018:8.

120 Dina K. Why Raw Works: The Food and Beauty Connection.

121 Tuso PJ, Ismail MH, Ha BP, Bartolotto C. Nutritional update for physicians: plant-based diets. The Permanente Journal. 2013;17(2):61.

122 Fardet A. A shift toward a new holistic paradigm will help to preserve and better process grain products' food structure for improving their health effects. Food & Function. 2015;6(2):363-82.

123 Elvira-Torales LI, García-Alonso J, Periago-Castón MJ. Nutritional importance of carotenoids and their effect on liver health: A review. Antioxidants. 2019 Jul;8(7):229.

124 Popova A, Mihaylova D. Antinutrients in plant-based foods: A review. The Open Biotechnology Journal. 2019 Jul 29;13(1).

125 Willcox DC, Willcox BJ, Todoriki H, Suzuki M. The Okinawan diet: health implications of a low-calorie, nutrient-dense, antioxidant-rich dietary pattern low in glycemic load. Journal of the American College of Nutrition. 2009 Aug 1;28(sup4):500S-16S.

126 Bender AE, Reaidi GB. Toxicity of kidney beans (Phaseolus vulgaris) with particular reference to lectins. Journal of plant foods. 1982 Mar 1;4(1):15-22.

127 Guenther PM, Dodd KW, Reedy J, Krebs-Smith SM. Most Americans eat much less than recommended amounts of fruits and vegetables. Journal of the American Dietetic Association. 2006 Sep 1;106(9):1371-9.

128 Ibid.

129 Kaur C, Kapoor HC. Antioxidants in fruits and vegetables–the millennium's health. International journal of food science & technology. 2001 Oct 20;36(7):703-25.

130 Craig WJ. Phytochemicals: guardians of our health. Journal of the American Dietetic Association. 1997 Oct 1;97(10):S199-204.

131 Holopainen JK, Kivimäenpää M, Julkunen-Tiitto R. New light for phytochemicals. Trends in biotechnology. 2018 Jan 1;36(1):7-10.

132 Pennington JA, Fisher RA. Classification of fruits and vegetables. Journal of Food Composition and Analysis. 2009 Dec 1;22:S23-31.

133 Nyamai DW, Arika W, Ogola PE, Njagi EN, Ngugi MP. Medicinally important phytochemicals: an untapped research avenue. Journal of pharmacognosy and phytochemistry. 2016 Mar;4(4):2321-6182.

134 Lengai GM, Muthomi JW, Mbega ER. Phytochemical activity and role of botanical pesticides in pest management for sustainable agricultural crop production. Scientific African. 2020 Mar 1;7:e00239.

135 Chen SS, Michael A, Butler-Manuel SA. Advances in the treatment of ovarian cancer—A potential role of anti-inflammatory phytochemicals. Discovery medicine. 2012 Jan 16;13(68):7-17.

136 Khan A, Suleman M, Abdul Baqi S, Ayub M. 1. Phytochemicals and their role in curing fatal diseases: A Review. Pure and Applied Biology (PAB). 2019 Feb 28;8(1):343-54.

137 Bian ZH, Yang QC, Liu WK. Effects of light quality on the accumulation of phytochemicals in vegetables produced in controlled environments: a review. Journal of the Science of Food and Agriculture. 2015 Mar 30;95(5):869-77.

138 Liu RH. Health benefits of fruit and vegetables are from additive and synergistic combinations of phytochemicals. The American journal of clinical nutrition. 2003 Sep 1;78(3):517S-20S.

139 McRorie Jr JW. Evidence-based approach to fiber supplements and clinically meaningful health benefits, part 1: what to look for and how to recommend an effective fiber therapy. Nutrition today. 2015 Mar;50(2):82.

140 Watson RR, Leonard TK. Selenium and vitamins A, E, and C: nutrients with cancer prevention properties. Journal of the American Dietetic Association. 1986 Apr 1;86(4):505-10.

141 Cai Y, Li Y, Wang R, Wu H, Chen Z, Zhang J, Ma Z, Hao X, Zhao Y, Zhang C, Huang F. A well-mixed phase formed by two compatible non-fullerene acceptors enables ternary organic solar cells with efficiency over 18.6%. Advanced Materials. 2021 Aug;33(33):2101733.

142 Lee SJ, Park CS, Kim BJ, Lee CS, Cha B, Lee YJ, Soh M, Park JA, Young PS, Song EH. Association between morningness and resilience in Korean college students. Chronobiology international. 2016 Nov 25;33(10):1391-9.

143 Sun SS, Liang R, Huang TT, Daniels SR, Arslanian S, Liu K, Grave GD, Siervogel RM. Childhood obesity predicts adult metabolic syndrome: the Fels Longitudinal Study. The Journal of pediatrics. 2008 Feb 1;152(2):191-200.

144 Garibyan L, Fisher DE. How sunlight causes melanoma. Current oncology reports. 2010 Sep;12(5):319-26.

145 John EM, Dreon DM, Koo J, Schwartz GG. Residential sunlight exposure is associated with a decreased risk of prostate cancer. The Journal of steroid biochemistry and molecular biology. 2004 May 1;89:549-52.

146 Johnson RS, Titze J, Weller R. Cutaneous control of blood pressure. Current opinion in nephrology and hypertension. 2016 Jan;25(1):11.

147 Lambert GW, Reid C, Kaye DM, Jennings GL, Esler MD. Effect of sunlight and season on serotonin turnover in the brain. The Lancet. 2002 Dec 7;360(9348):1840-2.

148 Nall R. What are the benefits of sunlight? Healthline https://www. Healthline. Com/health/depression/benefits-sunlight# mental-health Accessed. 2019 Aug;10.

149 Thor P, Krolczyk G, Gil K, Zurowski D, Nowak L. Melatonin and serotonin effects. J Physiol Pharmacol. 2007;58:97-105.

150 Dijk DJ, Cajochen C. Melatonin and the circadian regulation of sleep initiation, consolidation, structure, and the sleep EEG. Journal of biological rhythms. 1997 Dec;12(6):627-35.

151 Kraemer WJ, Noble BJ, Clark MJ, Culver BW. Physiologic responses to heavy-resistance exercise with very short rest periods. International journal of sports medicine. 1987 Aug;8(04):247-52.

152 Kass LR. Ageless bodies, happy souls: biotechnology and the pursuit of perfection. The New Atlantis. 2003 Apr 1(1):9-28.

153 Cincotta J. Light up Your Health: Understanding the Impact of Sunlight Exposure and Artificial Light on Health and Well-Being.

154 Kohyama J. A newly proposed disease condition produced by light exposure during night: Asynchronization. Brain and Development. 2009 Apr 1;31(4):255-73.

155 Bryant PA, Trinder J, Curtis N. Sick and tired: does sleep have a vital role in the immune system? Nature Reviews Immunology. 2004 Jun;4(6):457-67.

156 Coelho J, Lopez R, Richaud A, Buysse DJ, Wallace ML, Philip P, Micoulaud-Franchi JA. Toward a multi-lingual diagnostic tool for the worldwide problem of sleep health: The French RU-SATED validation. Journal of psychiatric research. 2021 Nov 1;143:341-9.

157 Jackson ML, Howard ME, Barnes M. Cognition and daytime functioning in sleep-related breathing disorders. Progress in brain research. 2011 Jan 1;190:53-68.

158 Nowson CA, McGrath JJ, Ebeling PR, Haikerwal A, Daly RM, Sanders KM, Seibel MJ, Mason RS. Vitamin D and health in adults in Australia and New Zealand: a position statement. Medical Journal of Australia. 2012 Jun;196(11):686-7.

159 Borkum JM. Migraine triggers and oxidative stress: a narrative review and synthesis. Headache: The Journal of Head and Face Pain. 2016 Jan;56(1):12-35.

160 MacKie RM, Elwood JM, Hawk JL. Links between exposure to ultraviolet radiation and skin cancer: a report of the Royal College of Physicians. Journal of the Royal College of Physicians of London. 1987 Apr;21(2):91.

161 Pail G, Huf W, Pjrek E, Winkler D, Willeit M, Praschak-Rieder N, Kasper S. Bright-light therapy in the treatment of mood disorders. Neuropsychobiology. 2011;64(3):152-62.

162 Smilowska K, Van Wamelen DJ, Schoutens A, Meinders MJ, Bloem BR. Blue light therapy glasses in Parkinson's disease: patients' experience. Parkinson's Disease. 2019 Jun 18;2019.

163 Strong RE, Marchant BK, Reimherr FW, Williams E, Soni P, Mestas R. Narrow-band blue-light treatment of seasonal affective disorder in adults and the influence of additional nonseasonal symptoms. Depression and anxiety. 2009 Mar;26(3):273-8.

164 Van Maanen A, Meijer AM, van der Heijden KB, Oort FJ. The effects of light therapy on sleep problems: a systematic review and meta-analysis. Sleep medicine reviews. 2016 Oct 1;29:52-62.

165 Glickman G, Byrne B, Pineda C, Hauck WW, Brainard GC. Light therapy for seasonal affective disorder with blue narrow-band light-emitting diodes (LEDs). Biological psychiatry. 2006 Mar 15;59(6):502-7.

166 Lougheed T. Hidden blue hazard? LED lighting and retinal damage in rats. 2014.

167 White S, White G. Slave clothing and African-American culture in the eighteenth and nineteenth centuries. Past & present. 1995 Aug 1(148):149-86.

168 Miller ML. Slaves to fashion. Duke University Press; 2009 Oct 8.

169 Brew ML. AMERICAN CLOTHING CONSUMPTION, 1879—1909. The University of Chicago; 1946.

170 McKay GD, Goldie PA, Payne WR, Oakes BW. Ankle injuries in basketball: injury rate and risk factors. British journal of sports medicine. 2001 Apr 1;35(2):103-8.

171 Meisler JG. Toward optimal health: the experts discuss foot care. 1998.

172 Mishra E, Jena S, Bhoi C, Arunachalam T, Panda SK. Effect of high heel gait on hip and knee-ankle-foot rollover characteristics while walking over inclined surfaces—A pilot study. The Foot. 2019 Sep 1;40:8-13.

173   Zöllner AM, Pok JM, McWalter EJ, Gold GE, Kuhl E. On high heels and short muscles: a multiscale model for sarcomere loss in the gastrocnemius muscle. Journal of theoretical biology. 2015 Jan 21;365:301-10.

174   O'Hern M. "Hugged as a viper to the bosom": Antebellum corset reform and the question of authority (Doctoral dissertation, University of Maryland, College Park).

175   Liu S, Hammond SK, Rojas-Cheatham A. Concentrations and potential health risks of metals in lip products. Environmental Health Perspectives. 2013 Jun;121(6):705-10.

176   Pérez-Granados AM, Vaquero MP. Silicon, aluminium, arsenic and lithium: essentiality and human health implications. Journal of Nutrition Health and Aging. 2002 Jan 1;6(2):154-62.

177   Irigaray P, Newby JA, Clapp R, Hardell L, Howard V, Montagnier L, Epstein S, Belpomme D. Lifestyle-related factors and environmental agents causing cancer: an overview. Biomedicine & Pharmacotherapy. 2007 Dec 1;61(10):640-58.

178   Welling R, Beaumont JJ, Petersen SJ, Alexeeff GV, Steinmaus C. Chromium VI and stomach cancer: a meta-analysis of the current epidemiological evidence. Occupational and environmental medicine. 2015 Feb 1;72(2):151-9.

179   Finkelstein Y, Markowitz ME, Rosen JF. Low-level lead-induced neurotoxicity in children: an update on central nervous system effects. Brain Research Reviews. 1998 Jul 1;27(2):168-76.

180   Pinto E, Paiva K, Carvalhido A, Almeida A. Elemental impurities in lipsticks: results from a survey of the Portuguese and Brazilian markets. Regulatory Toxicology and Pharmacology. 2018 Jun 1;95:307-13.

181   Rai A, Agarwal S, Bharti S, Ambedakar BB. Postural effect of back packs on school children: its consequences on their body posture. Int J Health Sci Res. 2013;3(10):109-6.

182   Foster RA. Male genital system. Jubb, Kennedy & Palmer's Pathology of Domestic Animals: Volume 3. 2016:465.

183   Grossman MG, Ducey SA, Nadler SS, Levy AS. Meralgia paresthetica: diagnosis and treatment. JAAOS-Journal of the American Academy of Orthopaedic Surgeons. 2001 Sep 1;9(5):336-44.

184   Bessa O. Tight pants syndrome: a new title for an old problem and often encountered medical problem. Archives of Internal Medicine. 1993 Jun 14;153(11):1396.

185   Ito S. High-intensity interval training for health benefits and care of cardiac diseases-the key to an efficient exercise protocol. World journal of cardiology. 2019 Jul 26;11(7):171.

186   Shiraev T, Barclay G. Evidence based exercise: Clinical benefits of high intensity interval training. Australian family physician. 2012 Dec;41(12):960-2.

187   Smith AE, Walter AA, Graef JL, Kendall KL, Moon JR, Lockwood CM, Fukuda DH, Beck TW, Cramer JT, Stout JR. Effects of β-alanine supplementation and high-intensity interval training on endurance performance and body composition in men; a double-blind trial. Journal of the International Society of Sports Nutrition. 2009 Dec;6(1):1-9.

188   Ito S. High-intensity interval training for health benefits and care of cardiac diseases-the key to an efficient exercise protocol. World journal of cardiology. 2019 Jul 26;11(7):171.

189   Smirmaul BP, Arena R. The urgent need to sit less and move more during the COVID-19 pandemic. Journal of cardiopulmonary rehabilitation and prevention. 2020 Sep;40(5):287.

190   Moffet H, Hagberg M, Hansson-Risberg E, Karlqvist LJ. Influence of laptop computer design and working position on physical exposure variables. Clinical Biomechanics. 2002 Jun 1;17(5):368-75.

191   Tumblin J, Turk G. LCIS: A boundary hierarchy for detail-preserving contrast reduction. InProceedings of the 26th annual conference on Computer graphics and interactive techniques 1999 Jul 1 (pp. 83-90).

192   Durairajanayagam D, Sharma RK, Plessis SS, Agarwal A. Testicular heat stress and sperm quality. InMale infertility 2014 (pp. 105-125). Springer, New York, NY.

193   Pelaseyed T, Bergström JH, Gustafsson JK, Ermund A, Birchenough GM, Schütte A, van der Post S, Svensson F, Rodríguez-Piñeiro AM, Nyström EE, Wising C. The mucus and mucins of the goblet cells and enterocytes provide the first defense line of the gastrointestinal tract and interact with the immune system. Immunological reviews. 2014 Jul;260(1):8-20.

194   Maher-Loughnan GP, MacDonald N, Mason AA, Fry L. Controlled trial of hypnosis in the symptomatic treatment of asthma. British Medical Journal. 1962 Aug 11;2(5301):371.

195   Willits RK, Saltzman WM. Synthetic polymers alter the structure of cervical mucus. Biomaterials. 2001 Mar 1;22(5):445-52.

196   Ijssennagger N, Belzer C, Hooiveld GJ, Dekker J, van Mil SW, Müller M, Kleerebezem M, van der Meer R. Gut microbiota facilitates dietary heme-induced epithelial hyperproliferation by opening the mucus barrier in colon. Proceedings of the National Academy of Sciences. 2015 Aug 11;112(32):10038-43.

197   Cher I. A new look at lubrication of the ocular surface: fluid mechanics behind the blinking eyelids. The ocular surface. 2008 Apr 1;6(2):79-86.

198   Lichtenberger LM. The hydrophobic barrier properties of gastrointestinal mucus. Annual review of physiology. 1995 Mar;57(1):565-83.

199   Wang BX, Wu CM, Ribbeck K. Home, sweet home: how mucus accommodates our microbiota. The FEBS journal. 2021 Mar;288(6):1789-99.

200   Wlodarska M, Luo C, Kolde R, d'Hennezel E, Annand JW, Heim CE, Krastel P, Schmitt EK, Omar AS, Creasey EA, Garner AL. Indoleacrylic acid produced by commensal peptostreptococcus species suppresses inflammation. Cell host & microbe. 2017 Jul 12;22(1):25-37.

201   Lopez E, Shattock RJ, Kent SJ, Chung AW. The multifaceted nature of immunoglobulin A and its complex role in HIV. AIDS research and human retroviruses. 2018 Sep 1;34(9):727-38.

202   Maresso AW. Innate Immunological Defenses Against Bacterial Attack. InBacterial Virulence 2019 (pp. 31-46). Springer, Cham.

203   Mileti DS, Sorensen JH. Communication of emergency public warnings. Landslides. 1990 Aug;1(6):52-70.

204 Gupta R. Absence of Interleukin-6 Protects Bone Marrow Erythroid Recovery Under Inflammation, a Process Inhibited by Iron Mediated ROS (Reactive Oxygen Species) Upregulation (Doctoral dissertation, Weill Medical College of Cornell University). 2017.

205 Fissel JA. THE INFLUENCE OF BACE1 EXPRESSION ON THE RECRUITMENT OF MACROPHAGES TO THE INJURED PERIPHERAL NERVE (Doctoral dissertation, Johns Hopkins University). 2020.

206 Irimia D, Wang X. Inflammation-on-a-chip: probing the system ex vivo. Trends in biotechnology. 2018 Sep 1;36(9):9 23-37.

207 Chang C, Gershwin immune ME. Integrative medicine in allergy and immunology. Clinical reviews in allergy & immunology. 2013 Jun;44(3):208-28.

208 Delgado AV, McManus AT, Chambers JP. Production of tumor necrosis factor-alpha, interleukin 1-beta, interleukin 2, and interleukin 6 by rat leukocyte subpopulations after exposure to substance P. Neuropeptides. 2003 Dec 1;37(6):355-61.

209 Nicholson LB. The immune system. Essays in biochemistry. 2016 Oct 31;60(3):275-301.

210 Bultman MW, Fisher FS, Pappagianis D. The ecology of soil-borne human pathogens. InEssentials of medical geology 2013 (pp. 477-504). Springer, Dordrecht.

211 Huang Y, Leobandung W, Foss A, Peppas NA. Molecular aspects of muco-and bioadhesion: Tethered structures and site-specific surfaces. Journal of controlled release. 2000 Mar 1;65(1-2):63-71.

212 Sirisinha S. The potential impact of gut microbiota on your health: Current status and future challenges. Asian Pac J Allergy Immunol. 2016 Dec 1;34(4):249-64.

213 Stanford J, Charlton K, Stefoska-Needham A, Zheng H, Bird L, Borst A, Fuller A, Lambert K. Associations among plant-based diet quality, uremic toxins, and gut microbiota profile in adults undergoing hemodialysis therapy. Journal of Renal Nutrition. 2021 Mar 1;31(2):177-88.

214 Anagnostopoulos DA, Tsaltas D. Fermented foods and beverages. InInnovations in Traditional Foods 2019 Jan 1 (pp. 257-291). Woodhead Publishing.

215 STORY M. How I Cured My Crohn's Disease.

216 Wastyk HC, Fragiadakis GK, Perelman D, Dahan D, Merrill BD, Feiqiao BY, Topf M, Gonzalez CG, Van Treuren W, Han S, Robinson JL. Gut-microbiota-targeted diets modulate human immune status. Cell. 2021 Aug 5;184(16):4137-53.

217 Markel H. John Harvey Kellogg and the pursuit of wellness. JAMA. 2011 May 4;305(17):1814-5.

218 Edlund A, Santiago-Rodriguez TM, Boehm TK, Pride DT. Bacteriophage and their potential roles in the human oral cavity. Journal of oral microbiology. 2015 Jan 1;7(1):27423.

219 Buonanno G, Stabile L, Morawska L. Estimation of airborne viral emission: Quanta emission rate of SARS-CoV-2 for infection risk assessment. Environment international. 2020 Aug 1;141:105794.

220 Baraniuk JN. Subjective nasal fullness and objective congestion. Proceedings of the American Thoracic Society. 2011 Mar 1;8(1):62-9.

221 Jones MG, Tretter T, Taylor A, Oppewal T. Experienced and novice teachers' concepts of spatial scale. International Journal of Science Education. 2008 Feb 26;30(3):409-29.

222 Zhang N, Chen W, Chan PT, Yen HL, Tang JW, Li Y. Close contact behavior in indoor environment and transmission of respiratory infection. Indoor air. 2020 Jul;30(4):645-61.

223 Sanchis-Gomar F, Lavie CJ, Mehra MR, Henry BM, Lippi G. Obesity and outcomes in COVID-19: when an epidemic and pandemic collide. InMayo Clinic Proceedings 2020 Jul 1 (Vol. 95, No. 7, pp. 1445-1453). Elsevier.

224 Mytton OT, Boyland E, Adams J, Collins B, O'Connell M, Russell SJ, Smith K, Stroud R, Viner RM, Cobiac LJ. The potential health impact of restricting less-healthy food and beverage advertising on UK television between 05.30 and 21.00 hours: A modelling study. PLoS medicine. 2020 Oct 13;17(10):e1003212.

225 Ojiogu AN, Onyia FC. TESTICULAR AND HEPATIC TOXICITY OF MONOSODIUM GLUTAMATE ON ADULT WISTAR RATS (Doctoral dissertation, Godfrey Okoye University).

226 Gibbs WW. Gaining on fat. Scientific American. 1996 Aug 1;275(2):88-94.

227 Sanigorski AM, Bell AC, Swinburn BA. Association of key foods and beverages with obesity in Australian schoolchildren. Public health nutrition. 2007 Feb;10(2):152-7.

228 Coon KA, Tucker KL. Television and children's consumption patterns. Minerva Pediatr. 2002;54(5):423-36.

229 Kiefer I, Rathmanner T, Kunze M. Eating and dieting differences in men and women. Journal of Men's Health and Gender. 2005 Jun;2(2):194-201.

230 Schreier H, Chen E. Socioeconomic status and the health of youth: a multilevel, multidomain approach to conceptualizing pathways. Psychological bulletin. 2013 May;139(3):606.

231 Cleator J, Abbott J, Judd P, Sutton C, Wilding JP. Night eating syndrome: implications for severe obesity. Nutrition & diabetes. 2012 Sep;2(9):e44-.

232 Kardan O, Gozdyra P, Misic B, Moola F, Palmer LJ, Paus T, Berman MG. Neighborhood greenspace and health in a large urban center. Scientific reports. 2015 Jul 9;5(1):1-4.

233 Ulrich RS. View through a window may influence recovery from surgery. Science. 1984 Apr 27;224(4647):420-1.

234 Willig AL, Morrow C, Rodriguez M, Overton E. Diet Quality and Obesity Impact Gut Microbial Composition in Older Adults Living with HIV (E02-01).

235 Paturi G, Butts CA, Bentley-Hewitt KL. Influence of dietary avocado on gut health in rats. Plant Foods for Human Nutrition. 2017 Sep;72(3):321-3.

236 Carranza-Madrigal J, Herrera-Abarca JE, Alvizouri-Muñoz M, Alvarado-Jimenez MD, Chavez-Carbajal F. Effects of a vegetarian diet vs. a vegetarian diet enriched with avocado in hypercholesterolemic patients. Archives of medical research. 1997 Jan 1;28(4):537-41.

237 Zhu L, Huang Y, Edirisinghe I, Park E, Burton-Freeman B. Using the avocado to test the satiety effects of a fat-fiber combination in place of carbohydrate energy in a breakfast meal in overweight and obese men and women: a randomized clinical trial. Nutrients. 2019 May;11(5):952.

238 Wing YM, Yu BM, Ming HW. Use of food waste, fish waste and food processing waste for China's aquaculture industry: Needs and challenge. Science of The Total Environment. 2018;635-643.

239 Eaton BS, M, Shostak M. Stone agers in the fast lane: Chronic degenerative diseases in evolutionary perspective. The American Journal of Medicine. 1988; 739-749.

240 Seligman MEP, Pawelski JO. Positive Psychology: FAQs. Psychological 2003;14(2), 159–163.

241 Foley PB. Dopamine in psychiatry: a historical perspective. J Neural Transm. 2019;126, 473–479.

242 Michely J, Viswanathan S, Hauser TU. The role of dopamine in dynamic effort-reward integration. Neuropsychopharmacol. 2020;45, 1448–1453.

243 Dobkin BH, Dorsch A. New Evidence for Therapies in Stroke Rehabilitation. Curr Atheroscler Rep. 2013;15, 331.

244 Wang GJ, Geliebter A, Volkow ND, Telang FW, Logan J, Jane MC, Galanti K, Selig PA, Han H, Zhu W, Wong CT, Fowler JS. Enhanced Striatal Dopamine Release During Food Stimulation in Binge Eating Disorder. Obesity. 2011;19: 1601-1608.

245 Stark C. The Impact of Sexual Satisfaction on the Relationship Between Work-Life Balance and Workplace Wellbeing. Adler University. ProQuest Dissertations Publishing, 2020. 28001865.

246 Pompili M, Lester D, Innamorati M, Tatarelli R, Girardi P. Assessment and treatment of suicide risk in schizophrenia. Expert Rev Neurother. 2008;8(1):51-74.

247 Rueve ME, Welton RS. Violence and mental illness. Psychiatry (Edgmont). 2008;5(5):34-48.

248 "Mead MN. Benefits of sunlight: a bright spot for human health [published correction appears in Environ Health Perspect. 2008 May;116(5):A197].

249 Meeusen R, Piacentini MF, Meirleir KD. Brain Microdialysis in Exercise Research. Sports Med 31, 2001; 965–983

250 Stasi C, Bellini M, Bassotti G. Serotonin receptors and their role in the pathophysiology and therapy of irritable bowel syndrome. Tech Coloproctol. 2014; 18, 613–621.

251 Katri P, Nora S, Riitta K. Diet promotes sleep duration and quality, Nutrition Research. 2012; Pages 309-319.

252 Thielke LE, Udell MAR. The role of oxytocin in relationships between dogs and humans and potential applications for the treatment of separation anxiety in dogs. Biol Rev, 2017; 92: 378-388.

253 Moira M, Nicolas P, Anthony L, De Timary P, Olivier L. Oxytocin not only increases trust when money is at stake, but also when confidential information is in the balance, Biological Psychology. 2010, Pages 182-184, 184.

254 Kathleen, CL Karen MG, Janet AA. More frequent partner hugs and higher oxytocin levels are linked to lower blood pressure and heart rate in premenopausal women. Biological Psychology, 2005; Vol 69(1):Pages 5-21.

255 Boccia ML, Melton K, Larson M. An overview of the use of oxytocin measures in leisure studies, Journal of Leisure Research, 2020; 51:3, 366-376.

256 Chirag S, Swarna A. Happy Chemicals and How to Hack Them. 2021 May 3.

257 Trappe H. The effects of music on the cardiovascular system and cardiovascular health. Heart 2010;96:1868-1871.

258 Mathew J, Paulose CS. The healing power of well-being. Acta Neuropsychiatrica. Cambridge University Press; 2011;23(4):145–55.

259 Berk R. THE ACTIVE INGREDIENTS IN HUMOR: PSYCHOPHYSIOLOGICAL BENEFITS AND RISKS FOR OLDER ADULTS, Educational Gerontology.2021; 27:3-4, 323-339.

260 Babar A, Naser AA, Saiba S, Aftab A, Shah AK, Firoz A. Essential oils used in aromatherapy: A systemic review, Asian Pacific Journal of Tropical Biomedicine. 2015; Vol 5(8) Pg:601-611.

261 Nathaniel MM. Benefits of sunlight: a bright spot for human health Environmental health perspectives. 2008;116 (4), A160-A167

262 Harber VJ, Sutton JR. Endorphins and Exercise. Sports Medicine. 1984;1, 154–171.

263 Souvik D, Payel B, Ritwik G, Subhankar C, Mahua JD, Subham C, Durjoy L, Carl JL. Psychosocial impact of COVID-19, Diabetes & Metabolic Syndrome: Clinical Research & Review. 2020; Vol 14:5.

264 Himle JA, Chatters LM, Taylor RJ, Nguyen A. The relationship between obsessive-compulsive disorder and religious faith: Clinical characteristics and implications for treatment. Psychology of Religion and Spirituality. 2011 3(4), 241–258.

265 Goldschmid V. Can Gratitude Help Your Bones And Your Health? 2015, November 23.

266 Emmons RA, Stern R. Gratitude as a Psychotherapeutic Intervention. J. Clin. Psychol., 2013; 69: 846-855.

267 Alex MW, Jeffrey JF, Adam WA. Gratitude and well-being: A review and theoretical integration, Clinical Psychology Review. 2010;30:7, 890-905.

268 Sheldon KM, Lyubomirsky S. How to increase and sustain positive emotion: The effects of expressing gratitude and visualizing best possible selves, The Journal of Positive Psychology. 2006;1:2, 73-82.

269 Waters L. A Review of School-Based Positive Psychology Interventions. The Australian Educational and Developmental Psychologist. Cambridge University Press; 2011;28(2):75–90.

Made in USA - North Chelmsford, MA
1311796_9781955866033
04.18.2022 1539